THE BOOK OF

FACTS

SUBTRACTION

A Comprehensive Guide for Teaching
Subtraction Facts

JAMES BURNETT
CALVIN IRONS
ALLAN TURTON

ORIGO
EDUCATION

The Book of Facts: Subtraction

Copyright 2007 ORIGO Education
Authors: James Burnett, Calvin Irons, and Allan Turton

Burnett, James.
The book of facts: subtraction.

ISBN 978 1 921023 44 6.
ISBN 1 921023 44 9.

1. Subtraction - Study and teaching. 2. Subtraction - Problems,
exercises, etc. I. Irons, Calvin J. II. Turton, Allan. III. Title.

512.92

For more information visit www.origoeducation.com.

ISBN: 978 1 921023 44 6

10 9 8 7 6 5 4 3

Printed and Bound in Malaysia for Imago

Contents

Introduction

BASIC FACTS

It is essential that all students are able to successfully calculate both mentally and with paper and pencil. The first significant step for calculating involves learning the basic number facts associated with each operation. The term *basic facts* refers to those facts that most people are expected to know automatically. The basic addition facts (and related subtraction facts) range from $0 + 0 = 0$ to $9 + 9 = 18$ inclusive. The basic multiplication facts (and related division facts) range from $0 \times 0 = 0$ to $9 \times 9 = 81$ inclusive. These facts form the basis for all future number work.

Research shows that the most effective way for students to learn the basic facts is to arrange the facts into *clusters*. Each cluster is based on a *thinking strategy* that students can use to help them learn all of the facts in that cluster (Fuson, 2003; Thornton, 1990). For example, *use doubles* is one of the addition clusters. Within that cluster are double facts and facts that involve doubling then adding 1 or 2.

In addition to teaching thinking strategies, a modern mathematics curriculum should include many opportunities for students to use and expand their thinking skills. Discussing the understandings students have about numbers and encouraging them to think about numbers and use operations in new ways, promotes *number sense*. This type of thinking is an excellent foundation for all computation and encourages creative and flexible thinking that is compatible with mental computation.

About this Series

Each title in *The Book of Facts* series is designed to help teachers develop their students' abilities to automatically and accurately recall the basic facts for each operation. Although the clusters of facts are individually addressed, they form part of a teaching sequence. The thinking involved in learning one set of facts is a prerequisite to learning the next set.

Each cluster of facts begins with a brief background on the strategy along with some preparation activities. Each cluster is then broken down further according to the sub-strategies used (see the contents page of each book). Activities in each strategy and sub-strategy are sequenced according to the following four stages of teaching and learning:

INTRODUCE

Hands-on materials, stories, discussions, and familiar visual aids are used to introduce the strategy or sub-strategy.

REINFORCE

These activities make links between concrete and symbolic representations of the facts being examined. Students also reflect on how the strategy or sub-strategy works and the numbers to which it applies.

PRACTICE

Games, worksheets, and other activities provide students with opportunities to apply and demonstrate their knowledge of the facts. At this stage, the students should use mental computation only and fast recall is stressed.

About this Book

EXTEND

Students are encouraged to apply the strategy to numbers beyond the range of the basic number facts. The activities in this section are designed to further strengthen the students' number sense, or "feel" for numbers.

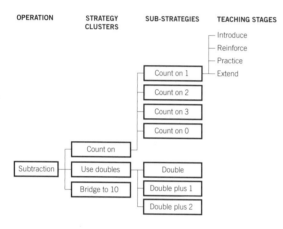

This diagram shows the general structure for *The Book of Facts: Subtraction*. Each book in the series covers one operation and involves grouping the facts into clusters around a thinking strategy and its sub-strategies. The most effective thinking strategy for subtraction is "use addition", therefore the strategies for the clusters of facts parallel those used for addition.

Each book in *The Book of Facts* series contains fully reproducible blackline masters. Some pages feature *Fact Files* that provide definitions and interesting facts relevant to the activities on the page. The series also complements the resources included in *The Box of Facts*. Many of the resources referenced in *The Book of Facts: Addition* and *The Book of Facts: Subtraction* are included in *The Box of Facts: Addition/Subtraction*. Illustrated references to these resources are made in relevant activities. These references enable quick identification for teachers who have the resources and provide blueprints for teachers who prefer to make their own.

Subtraction is the inverse operation of addition. Both operations involve a part-part-total structure but the known quantities vary. With addition, the parts are known but not the total; with subtraction, the total and one part are known, but not the other part. Because of this relationship between the two operations, *using addition* is the most effective thinking strategy for helping students to learn the basic subtraction facts.

In *The Book of Facts: Subtraction*, the strategies for the clusters of facts parallel those used for addition: *count on, use doubles*, and *bridge to 10*. The activities used in the first cluster also introduce the term *partner facts*. Where addition has *turnaround facts* such as $2 + 6 = 8$ and $6 + 2 = 8$, subtraction has *partner facts* such as $8 - 6 = 2$ and $8 - 2 = 6$. Addition facts and subtraction facts that involve the same parts and total form *fact families*.

The *count-on* strategy involves counting (not necessarily by ones) to add 1, 2, 3, or 0 to a given number. The count-on facts have at least one part that is 1, 2, 3, or 0. All sixty-four of the subtraction count-on facts are shown on page 3.

Known Part

−	0	1	2	3	4	5	6	7	8	9
0	0									
1	1	0								
2	2	1	0							
3	3	2	1	0						
4	4	3	2	1	0					
5	5	4	3	2	1	0				
6	6	5	4	3	2	1	0			
7	7	6	5	4	3	2	1	0		
8	8	7	6	5	4	3	2	1	0	
9	9	8	7	6	5	4	3	2	1	0
10		9	8	7	6	5	4	3	2	1
11			9	8	7	6	5	4	3	2
12				9	8	7	6	5	4	3
13					9	8	7	6	5	4
14						9	8	7	6	5
15							9	8	7	6
16								9	8	7
17									9	8
18										9

Total (row axis)

The orange shading in this table shows the count-on facts.

Known Part

−	0	1	2	3	4	5	6	7	8	9
0	0									
1	1	0								
2	2	1	0							
3	3	2	1	0						
4	4	3	2	1	0					
5	5	4	3	2	1	0				
6	6	5	4	3	2	1	0			
7	7	6	5	4	3	2	1	0		
8	8	7	6	5	4	3	2	1	0	
9	9	8	7	6	5	4	3	2	1	0
10		9	8	7	6	5	4	3	2	1
11			9	8	7	6	5	4	3	2
12				9	8	7	6	5	4	3
13					9	8	7	6	5	4
14						9	8	7	6	5
15							9	8	7	6
16								9	8	7
17									9	8
18										9

Total (row axis)

The orange shading in this table shows the use-doubles facts.

The *use-doubles* strategy involves doubling and doubling then adding 1 or 2. This strategy covers forty-four number facts as shown above right.

The tables above show that some basic facts are covered by both strategies. For example:

8 − 6 = 2 is only a count-on fact.
5 − 3 = 2 is a count-on and use-doubles fact.
11 − 5 = 6 is only a use-doubles fact.

The third strategy is called *bridge to 10*. As the name suggests, the idea is to start with one number, bridge the gap to 10 by using part of the second number, and then add the balance. Many of these facts are already covered by one of the first two strategies. The thirty-three bridge-to-10 facts are shaded in orange below.

When covering the basic facts the focus should be on mastering the facts, not matching facts with strategies. The strategies help break the total number of facts into manageable parts and provide a means for the students to recall the facts quickly and accurately. However, if a student is able to figure out a fact with speed and precision using a different strategy than the one suggested, then the goal has been accomplished.

Known Part

−	0	1	2	3	4	5	6	7	8	9
0	0									
1	1	0								
2	2	1	0							
3	3	2	1	0						
4	4	3	2	1	0					
5	5	4	3	2	1	0				
6	6	5	4	3	2	1	0			
7	7	6	5	4	3	2	1	0		
8	8	7	6	5	4	3	2	1	0	
9	9	8	7	6	5	4	3	2	1	0
10		9	8	7	6	5	4	3	2	1
11			9	8	7	6	5	4	3	2
12				9	8	7	6	5	4	3
13					9	8	7	6	5	4
14						9	8	7	6	5
15							9	8	7	6
16								9	8	7
17									9	8
18										9

Total

The orange shading in this table shows the bridge-to-10 facts.

Assessment

In *The Book of Facts: Subtraction*, several blackline masters can help teachers keep track of students' progress in mastering the basic facts. Blackline Masters 9 and 27 provide a formal means of assessment. The sheets fold into quarters so that the students see only one set of facts at a time. A reminder to use these sheets is given at the end of each *Practice* teaching and learning stage.

The following blackline masters can also be used to assess the facts covered in these sub-strategies (or strategy in the case of bridge to 10):

Count on 1:	Blackline Master 8
Count on 2:	Blackline Master 12
Count on 3:	Blackline Master 17
Count on 0:	Blackline Master 22
Double:	Blackline Master 26
Double plus 1:	Blackline Master 30
Double plus 2:	Blackline Master 32
Bridge to 10:	Blackline Master 34

The grid on Blackline Master 1 can be used to record student progress. The numerals in the first column on the left indicate the total involved in a subtraction fact. The numerals in the top row indicate the part to be subtracted (the known part). Where the row and column of these two numerals intersect is the result of the subtraction. A variety of markings, such as a simple ✓ or ✗, can be used to record whether a student can recall the fact both quickly and accurately. The Student Tracking Chart on Blackline Master 2 can then be used to record overall achievement for each student in the class.

The students will appreciate seeing the progress they make in covering the basic facts. Make an overhead transparency of Blackline Master 1 and as the class completes each strategy or sub-strategy, shade the relevant facts.

Known Part

–	0	1	2	3	4	5	6	7	8	9
0	0									
1	1	0								
2	2	1	0							
3	3	2	1	0						
4	4	3	2	1	0					
5	5	4	3	2	1	0				
6	6	5	4	3	2	1	0			
7	7	6	5	4	3	2	1	0		
8	8	7	6	5	4	3	2	1	0	
9	9	8	7	6	5	4	3	2	1	0
10		9	8	7	6	5	4	3	2	1
11			9	8	7	6	5	4	3	2
12				9	8	7	6	5	4	3
13					9	8	7	6	5	4
14						9	8	7	6	5
15							9	8	7	6
16								9	8	7
17									9	8
18										9

Total (label on left side)

To find the result of 11 – 5, locate the 11 in the first column on the left and the 5 in the top row. Where the row and column intersect is the missing part (6).

References

Fuson, K. C. (2003). Developing mathematical power in whole number operations. In J. Kilpatrick, W. G. Martin, & D. Schifter (Eds.), *A research companion to principles and standards for school mathematics* (pp. 68–94). Reston, VA: National Council of Teachers of Mathematics.

Thornton, C. (1990). Strategies for the basic facts. In J. N. Payne (Ed.), *Mathematics for the young child* (pp. 131–151). Reston, VA: National Council of Teachers of Mathematics.

Count On

Fact File

Both addition and subtraction have a part-part-total structure. In the operation of addition, two or more parts (*addends*) are added to form a total (*sum*). The values of the parts are known but the total is unknown.

$$7 \quad + \quad 5 \quad = \quad 12$$

addend   addend   sum

In subtraction, the values of the total (*minuend*) and one part (*subtrahend*) are known. The value of the second part (*difference*) is unknown.

$$12 \quad - \quad 7 \quad = \quad 5$$

minuend   subtrahend   difference

The facts covered in this strategy are related to the facts covered in the "count-on" strategy used in addition. As such, this strategy covers more than half of the basic subtraction facts. Many students will know what "take away" means when they begin to learn subtraction facts. Taking away works well when subtracting 1, 2, or 3. When the number to be subtracted is close to the total, it is easier to use addition to calculate the difference or missing addend. In both situations, the *think-addition* approach can be used. For example, to find the missing value in $12 - 9 = \rule{1cm}{0.4pt}$, encourage the students to think, "What do I add to 9 to make 12?" This type of thinking is introduced for the count-on strategy facts, beginning with the subtraction facts related to the count-on-1 addition facts.

Also introduced in the count-on cluster of facts is the idea of *partner facts* and *fact families*. Partner facts are pairs of subtraction facts that are related to an addition fact. For example, $12 - 9 = 3$ and $12 - 3 = 9$ are partner facts because they both relate to $9 + 3 = 12$ and its turnaround $3 + 9 = 12$. These four facts form a fact family.

Prepare

1 Write **6** on the board. Ask the students to write all of the addition facts they know that have a total of 6. Invite volunteers to share their answers. Record the answers on the board. Repeat with other numbers less than 10.

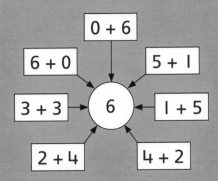

2 Direct each student to write a numeral from 0 to 9 and another from 10 to 19. Write **5 + 3 = 8** on the board. Erase one of the numerals in the number sentence and invite a student to say one of the numerals they wrote. Write the numeral in the vacant space and ask the class, *Is this addition fact still true? How do you know? What other number can we change to make it true?* Discuss the possibilities and then change the sentence as suggested. Afterward, erase another number and repeat the discussion.

3 Share some simple subtraction stories. Examples may include, *Six birds are sitting on the fence. Two fly away. How many birds are on the fence now?* or *I had four lollipops. I gave away one. How many lollipops do I have now?* As you say the stories, invite selected students to act them out using counters or cubes. Some students may like to share their own subtraction stories.

4 Use some of the stories from the previous activity and draw pictures on the board to represent the "take away" action. For example, draw four lollipops on the board and cross out one as you repeat the story. Repeat with other stories, then have each student write their own subtraction story and draw a simple picture to match. Invite volunteers to share their stories and pictures with the class.

Fact File

A *number* is used for counting, labeling, and ordering.

A *numeral* is the symbol used to represent a number.

An *expression* is a combination of numerals and operation symbols (e.g. 16 – 1).

A *number sentence* is a statement of the relationship between two or more expressions (e.g. 16 – 1 = 15).

5 Draw a simple pond on an overhead transparency as shown below. Place eight identical counters on the transparency as you say, *Five frogs are sitting in a pond. Three frogs are sitting beside the pond. How many frogs are there in total?* Write **5 + 3 = 8** on the board. Point to the number sentence and ask, *What number tells us how many frogs there are in total?* (Eight.) *What do the other numbers tell us?* Highlight how the five and three represent two groups of frogs (some in the pond and some beside it).

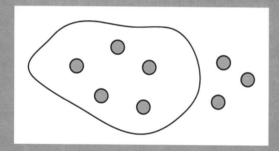

Place all of the counters in the pond and ask, *How many frogs are in the pond?* (Eight.) *Three frogs jump out. How many are left in the pond?* Write **8 – 3 = 5** on the board. Point to the number sentence and ask, *What number tells us how many frogs were originally in the pond?* (Eight.) *What do the other numbers tell us?* (The number of frogs in each group.) *What is the same about both stories?* (They both involve a total made up of two groups.) *What is different?* (In the addition story two groups join together to make a total. In the subtraction story the total splits into two groups.)

Give the students ten counters each and repeat with other subtraction stories. Ask the students to act out the stories using the counters before identifying the total and parts in each story.

Count On 1

Introduce

1 Make a cube train from four orange cubes. Display the train then add one white cube. Ask, What is an addition number sentence we can write to describe what the cubes show? Invite an individual to write **4 + 1 = 5** on the board. Ask, What is an addition story that matches this number sentence? Allow the students time to think of a story then invite an individual to share their story with the class. Allow them to use the cubes to show what happens.

Show the cube train again and remove the white cube. Ask, What is a subtraction number sentence we can write to describe what happened with the cubes? Invite a volunteer to write a suitable number sentence on the board ($5 - 1 = 4$) and encourage the students think of a story to match.

Repeat both steps with other quantities of orange cubes and one white cube.

2 On the board or an overhead transparency, draw a number line from 1 to 10 and write **7 – 1 = ___** below it. Ask, How can you figure out the missing part? Invite volunteers to describe and demonstrate their thinking using the number line.

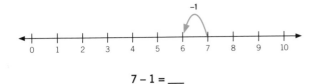

$$7 - 1 = \text{\_\_}$$

Draw a second number line and write **7 – 6 = ___** below it. Ask the students to think about how they can figure out the value of the missing part. Select individuals to show their thinking using the number line. Some students may count back by ones, until they have counted back 6.

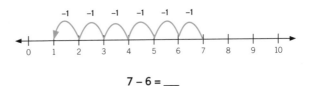

$$7 - 6 = \text{\_\_}$$

Others may notice that $7 - 6 = \text{\_\_}$ is the same as $6 + \text{\_\_} = 7$ and draw a jump of 1 from 6 to 7.

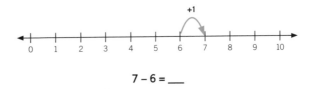

$$7 - 6 = \text{\_\_}$$

Repeat with other subtraction pairs that relate to a count-on-1 addition fact. Highlight how thinking of an addition fact then counting on can be faster than counting back by ones.

Fact File

The main approach for learning the subtraction facts is to "think addition". For this reason, clusters of subtraction facts are named according to the strategy used for the related addition facts. For example, $8 - 1 = 7$ is part of the count-on subtraction fact cluster, because its related addition fact $7 + 1 = 8$ involves counting on one.

3 ▶ Select or make the flip cards shown below.

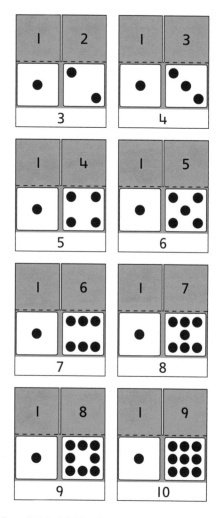

See: *Think-Addition Subtraction Strategy Cards*

Show the students the 1 + 5 card. Explain the following features:

- The card shows an addition fact.

- The numerals above the dots show how many dots there are on the left-hand and right-hand sides.

- The numeral at the bottom shows how many dots there are in total.

Ask, What are the two addition facts that this card shows? (One add five is six. Five add one is six.)

Hold the 1 + 3 card so that the flap showing 3 covers the three dots. Display the card to the students and ask, What do we know when we look at this card? (There are four dots in total, but only one is showing.)

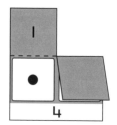

Ask, How can we figure out how many dots are covered? The students' suggestions may include, "I start with four and count back one to make three," or, "I know that one add three is four, so there must be three dots covered."

Repeat with other cards from the set. Use each card twice, folding a different flap each time.

Reinforce

Give each student a copy of Blackline Master 3. Ensure the students understand what to do then ask them to complete the sheet individually.

Make or select the addition flash cards shown below. Make a paper sleeve that can completely cover any symbol or numeral on the cards.

1 + 1 = 2	1 + 2 = 3	1 + 3 = 4
1 + 4 = 5	1 + 5 = 6	1 + 6 = 7
1 + 7 = 8	1 + 8 = 9	1 + 9 = 10

See: *Missing-Addend Subtraction Cards*

Select the 1 + 5 = 6 card and position the sleeve over the first addend as shown below. Display the card and ask, What is the number that is covered? How do you know? The students' responses may include, "I know that one and five is six, so the missing number must be one."

| + 5 = 6 |

Select the 1 + 7 = 8 card and position the sleeve over the second addend. Display the card and ask the students to figure out the missing number. The students' responses may include, "I know that one and seven is eight so the missing number is seven," or, "I know that the number is one less than eight. So I counted back one from eight and got seven."

Repeat with other cards as time allows, alternating between covering the first and second addends.

3 Make or select the dominoes shown below.

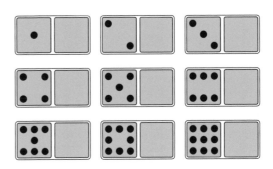

Display the domino showing six dots. Say, Think about this story. Seven friends are going to a movie. Six have arrived already. How many more need to arrive? Pause a moment then ask, What is the total number of friends going to the movie? (Seven.) How many have arrived already? (Six.) How many more dots should we draw to show the number of friends that need to arrive? How do you know? (One, because six add one is seven.) What addition sentence can we write to describe this story? Write 6 + ___ = 7 on the board.

Repeat with other dominoes and other stories. One of the parts that make the total should have a value of 1. For example:

"A car seats five people. Four people are in the car already. How many more people can fit in the car?"

"I have read one book. I have to read four books this week. How many more books do I need to read?"

4 Share this story with students, *I have one lollipop. I need a total of four lollipops to put into a party bag. How many more lollipops do I need to get?* Show the matching domino and discuss the story. Say, *We can use an addition sentence to show this story.* Write **1 + ___ = 4** on the board. Say, *We can also write a subtraction sentence to show this story. We will use a picture to help us.* On the board, draw four lollipops.

Say, *We know that we want four lollipops as a total. We already have one lollipop so we can cross that out. We need to figure out how many lollipops we still need to get. What subtraction sentence can we write to show this?* Invite a student to write **4 − 1 = ___** on the board.

Repeat with the other stories from the previous activity.

5 Give each student a copy of Blackline Master 4. Read the instructions and then ask the students to complete the sheet individually.

Practice

1 Select or make the double-sided flash cards shown below. Each card should show a subtraction fact (such as 3 − 1 = ___) on one side and its partner fact (3 − 2 = ___) on the other side. Show one card and select a student to say the missing part. Allow approximately three seconds for the student to respond. Repeat several times with other students and cards (including the partner facts).

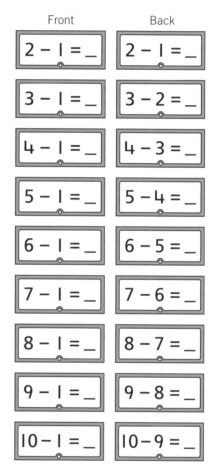

See: *Subtraction Flash Cards*

Fact File

Partner facts are pairs of subtraction facts that are related to an addition fact. For example, $12 - 9 = 3$ and $12 - 3 = 9$ are partner facts. They both relate to $9 + 3 = 12$ and its turnaround fact $3 + 9 = 12$. All four of these facts together form a *fact family*.

This is a game for two to four players. Give each group a copy of Blackline Masters 5 and 6, and a paper clip. Instruct the students to label the spinner segments 1, 1, 1, 1, 2, 3, 4, 5, and 6. The students should straighten the paper clip to make a spinner as shown below. Give each student four counters (a different color for each student). Direct them to use the top half of Blackline Master 6 as a game board.

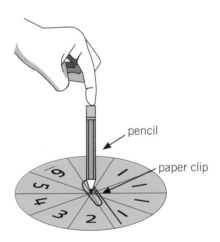

pencil

paper clip

To play the game:

- The first player spins the paper clip.

- The numeral that the paper clip tip rests on is the missing part from a number sentence. The player places a counter on a matching number sentence on the game board.

- Each of the other players has a turn.

- As the game continues, the player misses a turn if the matching number sentence is not available.

- The first player to place all four counters on the game board wins.

Once the students have played the game several times, direct them use the game board on the lower half of the sheet. Instruct them to label the segments of the other spinner 1, 1, 1, 1, 1, 5, 6, 7, 8, and 9. To avoid confusion between 6 and 9, have the students underline them.

3 As a variation of the previous activity, give each group of students a copy of Blackline Master 7. Direct them to use the game board on the top half of the sheet. The students can reuse the same counters and spinners. Repeat the activity using the game board on the lower half of the sheet.

4 Give each student a copy of Blackline Master 8. Read the instruction then ask the students to complete the sheet individually.

5 Give each student a copy of Blackline Master 9. Direct them to fold the sheet into quarters so that they can see only the *Count-On-1* section. This assessment task should take no more than two minutes for the students to complete. A longer period of time may indicate that recall of the facts is not automatic. Collect the sheets afterward and record the results for each student on Blackline Masters 1 and 2. See page 5 of the *Introduction* for instructions.

Extend

1 Draw the number line shown below on the board or on an overhead transparency. Ask, *What number could be at the start of the jump?* (35.) *If it is 35, what number will be at the other end of the jump? How do you know?* (Thirty-five subtract one is thirty-four.) Redraw the "jump" arrow in a different position and repeat the activity.

$$-1$$

```
  ←——————+————————+————————+——————→
         20       30       40
```

2 Write these empty number sentences on the board.

___ + ___ = ___   ___ – ___ = ___

___ + ___ = ___   ___ – ___ = ___

Write **17**, **1**, and **16** on the board and say, *Use only these three numbers in each sentence to make them true.* Allow the students some thinking time and then ask for suggestions. As you complete each sentence ask the students to describe how they decided where to place the numbers. Repeat the activity using other sets of three numbers. Make sure the number 1 is in each set.

3 Write these number sentences on the board.

$9 – 1 =$ ___ $10 – 1 =$ ___

$19 – 1 =$ ___ $20 – 1 =$ ___

$29 – 1 =$ ___ $30 – 1 =$ ___

$39 – 1 =$ ___ $40 – 1 =$ ___

Ask, *What are the missing parts? How do you know?* Encourage the students to use a variety of strategies to explain their thinking. Ask them to describe how they can use addition to figure out the answers. For example, they may say, "Twenty subtract one must be nineteen because nineteen plus one is twenty." Complete the number sentence as the students provide the answers. Ask, *What other number sentences can we write to keep the pattern going? How do you know the answers?*

Write these number sentences on the board and repeat the discussion.

$7 – 6 =$ ___ $9 – 8 =$ ___

$17 – 16 =$ ___ $19 – 18 =$ ___

$27 – 26 =$ ___ $29 – 28 =$ ___

$37 – 36 =$ ___ $39 – 38 =$ ___

Count On 2

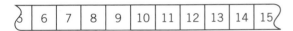

Introduce

▶ Draw a number track on the board from 1 to 20 inclusive. Ask the students to start at any number and count back in steps of 2. For example, start at 15 and count 13, 11, 9, 7, and so on. Repeat this activity as time allows. Each time, invite a volunteer to choose the starting number.

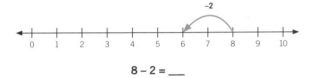

▶ Draw a number line from 1 to 10 on the board or on an overhead transparency and write **8 – 2 = ___** below it. Ask, How can you figure out the missing part? Invite volunteers to describe and demonstrate their thinking on the number line.

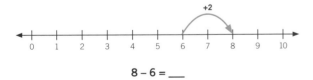

$$8 - 2 = \_\_$$

Draw a second number line and write **8 – 6 = ___** below it. Ask the students how they would figure out the value of the missing part. Select individuals to demonstrate their thinking on the number line. Some students may count back by ones, until they have counted back 6. Others may notice that 8 – 6 = ___ is the same as 6 + ___ = 8 and draw a jump of 2 from 6 to 8.

$$8 - 6 = \_\_$$

Repeat with other subtraction pairs that relate to a count-on-2 addition fact. Highlight how thinking of an addition fact then counting on is often faster than counting back by ones.

3 ▶ Make an overhead transparency of a double ten-frame. Say, Jacob has seven balloons and Taylor has two balloons. How many more balloons does Jacob have than Taylor? Ask a volunteer to use counters to represent the two quantities in the ten-frames. Retell the story, pointing to the two groups of counters, then cover two counters in each frame to reveal the difference between the groups. Ask a student to say the amount that is showing. Say, This amount tells us how many more balloons Taylor will need to have the same total as Jacob. Direct the class to write a related subtraction fact (7 – 2 = 5) and then repeat the activity using other stories involving 1 or 2.

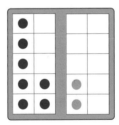

4 ▶ Give each pair of students a double ten-frame and twelve counters. Direct them to think of stories that involve a comparison between 2 and another number less than 10. Instruct them to write the matching number sentences for two of their stories. Call on volunteers to share their stories and demonstrate their thinking on an overhead transparency of a double ten-frame.

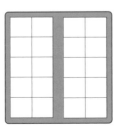

See: *Bridge-to-10 Frames*

5 Select or make the flip cards shown below.

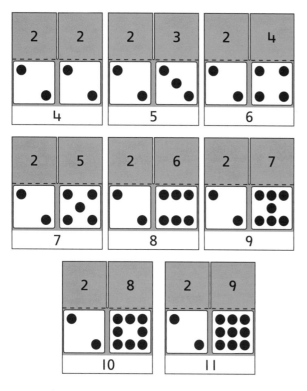

See: *Think-Addition Subtraction Strategy Cards*

Hold the 2 + 4 card so that the flap showing 4 covers the four dots. Display the card to the students and ask, What do we know when we look at this card? (There are six dots in total, but only two are showing.)

Ask, How can we figure out how many dots are covered? The students' suggestions may include, "I could start with six and count back two to make four," or, "I know that two add four is six, so four dots must be covered."

Repeat with the other cards. Use each card twice, folding a different flap each time.

Reinforce

1 Make or select the addition flash cards shown below. Make a paper sleeve that can completely cover any symbol or numeral on the cards.

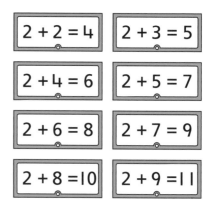

See: *Missing-Addend Subtraction Cards*

Select the 2 + 4 = 6 card and and position the sleeve over the first addend as shown below. Display the card and ask, Which number is covered? How do you know? The students may offer suggestions such as, "I know that two add four is six, so the missing number must be two."

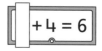

Select another card and position the sleeve over the second addend. Display the card and ask the students to figure out the missing number. The students' responses may include counting back 2 or using the related addition fact. Repeat with other cards as time allows, alternating between covering the first and second addends.

Read some count-on-1 and count-on-2 stories from Blackline Master 10. Ask the students to suggest matching number sentences for each story and to describe the thinking they used to figure them out. Afterward, give each student a copy of Blackline Master 11 and have them work individually to complete the sheet.

Draw the function machine shown below on an overhead transparency or on the board. Write **+1** in the middle of the machine. Explain to the students that the machine adds 1 to any number that goes into it. Write **7** as the IN number. Ask, If seven goes in, what number will come out? How do you know?

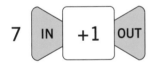

Repeat the activity by writing other IN numbers and **+2** in the middle of the machine. At a later time, write **−2** in the middle section and **5** as the IN number. Say, This machine subtracts two from any number that goes in. If five goes in the machine, what number will come out? Encourage the students to use thinking that involves both addition and subtraction. For example, "I know the answer is three because three and the two that I took away make five," or, "Start with five and count back two is three." After the students have explained their thinking for this example, ask them to suggest other numbers to put into the machine and discuss how they determine the OUT number.

Fact File

A function machine is also known as an *in/out* machine or *input/output* machine. It represents an imaginary machine that applies a rule to one number to produce another number. The function machine is ideal for using and reinforcing the inverse relationship between addition and subtraction.

4 Draw a function machine as shown below on the board. Write **−2** in the middle and **6** as the OUT number. Ask, What numbers does the machine tell you? (The two parts that make a total.) What number is unknown? (The original total or starting number.) What number sentence can we write to show this? Invite a volunteer to write ___ − 2 = 6 on the board.

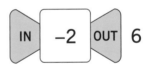

Ask, How can you figure out the missing number? Encourage the students to use both addition and subtraction in their explanations. Repeat the discussion for other IN and OUT numbers. Change the operation and numeral in the middle of the machine (only use +1, +2, −1, or −2) and repeat the activity.

Practice

1 Select or make the double-sided flash cards shown below (the partner fact is on the back of each card). The cards should be made of exactly the same paper as the other flash cards used previously. Show one card and select a student to say the missing part. Allow approximately three seconds for the student to respond. Repeat several times with other students and cards (including the partner facts).

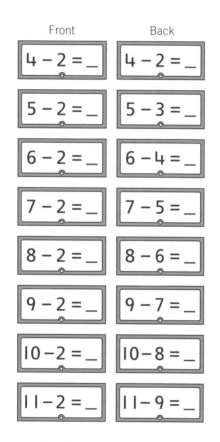

Front   Back

4 – 2 = _   4 – 2 = _

5 – 2 = _   5 – 3 = _

6 – 2 = _   6 – 4 = _

7 – 2 = _   7 – 5 = _

8 – 2 = _   8 – 6 = _

9 – 2 = _   9 – 7 = _

10 – 2 = _   10 – 8 = _

11 – 2 = _   11 – 9 = _

See: *Subtraction Flash Cards*

2 Give each student a copy of Blackline Master 12. Read the instruction and then ask the students to complete the sheet individually.

3 This is a game for two players. Give each pair of students a copy of Blackline Master 13 and two blank cubes. They will also need 20 counters in two different colors. Instruct the students to label the faces of one cube 1, 1, 1, 2, 2, and 2 and the faces of the other cube 6, 7, 8, 9, 10, and 11. The 6 and 9 should be underlined to avoid confusion. Only the top half of the Blackline Master 13 is used for this activity.

To play the game:

- The first player rolls both cubes.

- The player calculates the difference between the two numbers shown then places a counter on a matching space on the game board.

- The other player takes a turn.

- As the game continues, the player misses a turn if a matching space is not available.

- The first player to make a vertical, horizontal, or diagonal line of three adjacent counters wins.

Repeat the game using the lower half of Blackline Master 13. The cube labeled 6, 7, 8, 9, 10, and 11 can be reused with another cube labeled 5, 6, 7, 8, 9, and 10.

4 Distribute the students' record sheets from *Practice* Activity 5 on page 13 (Blackline Master 9). Direct them to fold the sheet so that they can see only the *Count-On-2* section. This assessment task should take no more than about $1\frac{1}{2}$ minutes for the students to complete. A longer period of time may indicate that recall of the facts is not automatic. Collect the sheets afterward and record the results for each student on Blackline Masters 1 and 2. See page 5 of the *Introduction* for instructions.

Extend

Write ___ − ___ = 2 on the board. Ask, *What numbers will make this sentence true? How did you decide?* Encourage the students to suggest different strategies. For example, they may say, "If one digit is an even number the other digit must be an even number that is just above or just below." Ask, *How can you rearrange the numbers to make another subtraction sentence that is true?*

Write ___ + ___ = ___ on the board and ask, *Where can you put the numbers from the subtraction sentence to make this addition sentence true? What is another addition sentence we can make using those numbers?* Repeat as time allows.

Draw a number line on the board as shown below. Mark a jump of +2 on it and ask, *What numbers could be at the beginning and end of the arrow? How did you decide?* As the students offer suggestions, ask them to suggest number sentences that help them to express the thinking they used. Repeat the activity with the arrow drawn in other positions.

On the board, draw the function machine shown. Ask, *What numbers does the machine tell you? What number is unknown? How can you figure out the missing number?* Encourage the students to use a variety of explanations using either addition or subtraction.

Repeat the discussion using other IN or OUT numbers between 22 and 28. Vary the activity by writing +1, +2, −1, or −2 in the middle of the machine.

Draw a function machine on the board or an overhead transparency sheet. Write −12 in the middle and 2 as the OUT number. Ask, *What must the IN number be to make two the OUT number? How do you know?* Suggestions may include, "Fourteen should be the IN number because twelve add two is fourteen." Change the amount in the middle and repeat. At other times, write the numeral 1 as the OUT number.

Fact File

The main approach for learning the subtraction facts is to "think addition". For this reason, clusters of subtraction facts are named according to the strategy used for the related addition facts. For example, 9 − 2 = 7 is part of the count-on subtraction fact cluster, because its related addition fact 7 + 2 = 9 involves counting on two.

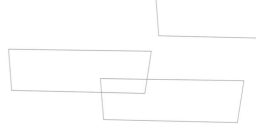

Count On 3

Introduce

1 ▶ Share some of the count-on-3 stories from Blackline Master 10 with the class. For each story, ask the students to describe which numbers are known, which number is unknown and how they might figure out the value of the missing quantity. Encourage the students to show their thinking using materials such as counters or cubes and to write a matching number fact. Afterward, the students can write two or three stories and then have a partner solve them.

2 ▶ Write **7** on the board. Ask, What number is three more than seven? What number is three less than seven? How do you know? As the students explain their thinking, draw a number track on the board as shown below. Repeat the activity using other numbers. Choose numbers that will complete the number track from 1 to 12.

		4		7		10		

3 ▶ Select or make the flip cards shown.

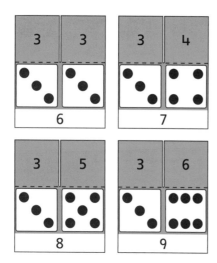

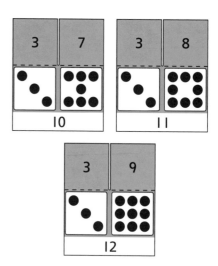

See: *Think-Addition Subtraction Strategy Cards*

Hold the 3 + 6 card so that the flap showing 6 covers the six dots. Display the card to the students and ask, What do we know when we look at this card? (There are nine dots in total, but only three are showing.) How can we figure out how many dots are covered? The students' suggestions may include, "I start with nine and count back three to make six," or, "I know that three add six is nine, so there must be six dots covered."

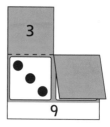

Repeat the activity with the other cards. Use each card twice, folding a different flap each time.

Reinforce

1 Make or select the addition flash cards shown below. Make a paper sleeve that can completely cover any symbol or numeral on the cards.

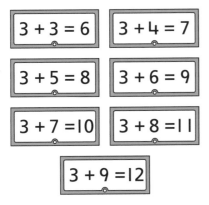

3 + 3 = 6	3 + 4 = 7
3 + 5 = 8	3 + 6 = 9
3 + 7 =10	3 + 8 =11
	3 + 9 =12

See: *Missing-Addend Subtraction Cards*

Select the 3 + 5 = 8 card and position the sleeve over the first addend as shown below. Display the card and ask, What number is covered? How do you know? The students may offer suggestions such as, "I know that three and five is eight, so the missing number must be three."

```
   + 5 = 8
```

Select another card and position the sleeve over the second addend. Display the card and ask the students to figure out the missing number. The students' responses may include counting back 3 or thinking of the related addition fact. Repeat with other cards as time allows, alternating between covering the first and second addends.

2 Copy Blackline Master 14 onto an overhead transparency. Select or make the dominoes shown below.

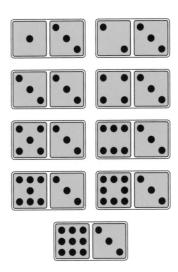

Display the domino with five and three dots. Ask, How many dots are there in total? (Eight.) How many dots are there in each part? (Five and three.) What are two addition facts that involve all of these numbers? Write **5 + 3 = 8** and **3 + 5 = 8** on the transparency. Ask, What are two subtraction facts that involve all of these numbers? Write **8 – 3 = 5** and **8 – 5 = 3** on the transparency. Say, All of these facts together make a fact family. They are all related because they involve the same numbers for the total and the parts that make the total.

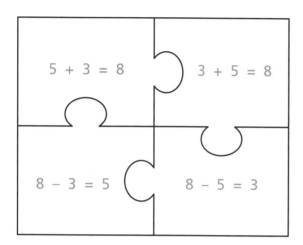

$$5 + 3 = 8 \qquad 3 + 5 = 8$$

$$8 - 3 = 5 \qquad 8 - 5 = 3$$

Erase the facts from the transparency. Show a different domino and ask the students to identify the facts that form the fact family to match. Record the results on the transparency then repeat with the other dominoes.

Fact File

Both addition and subtraction have a part-part-total structure. In the operation of addition, two or more parts (*addends*) are joined together to form a total (*sum*). The values of the parts are known but the total is unknown.

In subtraction, the values of the total (*minuend*) and one part (*subtrahend*) are known. The value of a second part (*difference*) is unknown.

3 Give each student a copy of Blackline Master 15. Read the instruction with the students before directing them to complete the page individually.

Practice

1 Select or make the double-sided flash cards shown below (the partner fact is on the back of each card). The cards should be made of exactly the same paper as the flash cards used previously. Show one card and select a student to identify the missing part. Allow approximately three seconds for the student to respond. Repeat several times with other students and cards (including the partner facts).

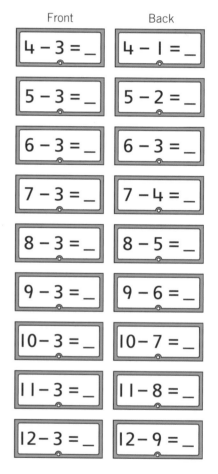

Front	Back
4 − 3 = _	4 − 1 = _
5 − 3 = _	5 − 2 = _
6 − 3 = _	6 − 3 = _
7 − 3 = _	7 − 4 = _
8 − 3 = _	8 − 5 = _
9 − 3 = _	9 − 6 = _
10 − 3 = _	10 − 7 = _
11 − 3 = _	11 − 8 = _
12 − 3 = _	12 − 9 = _

See: *Subtraction Flash Cards*

2 Give each student a copy of Blackline Master 16. Explain that these function machines can process many IN and OUT numbers at once. Work through a couple of examples with the students before directing them to complete the sheet individually.

3 The students can work in pairs for this activity. Give each pair a blank cube and instruct them to label the faces 1, 2, 3, 1, 2, and 3. Have the students take turns to roll the cube. They should write a subtraction fact that has a difference of the number rolled. For example, if the cube shows 2, the subtraction fact 9 − 7 = 2 can be written. Once a fact is written it cannot be used again.

4 Copy Blackline Master 17 for each student. Read the instruction and then direct the students to complete the sheet individually.

5 Distribute the students' record sheets used in *Practice* Activity 5 on page 13 (Blackline Master 9). Direct them to fold the sheet so that they can see only the *Count-On-3* section. This assessment task should take no more than $1\frac{1}{2}$ minutes for the students to complete. A longer period of time may indicate that recall of the facts is not automatic. Collect the sheets afterward and record the results for each student on Blackline Masters 1 and 2. See page 5 of the *Introduction* for instructions.

> **Fact File**
> The main approach for learning the subtraction facts is to "think addition". For this reason, clusters of subtraction facts are named according to the strategy used for the related addition facts. For example, 8 − 3 = 5 is part of the count-on subtraction fact cluster, because its related addition fact 5 + 3 = 8 involves counting on three.

Extend

1 On the board, draw the diagram shown below. Explain that the number written in the middle is the difference for three subtraction facts. Call on volunteers to suggest the missing total for each subtraction expression so that the result is 6. For example, 7 − 1 = 6.

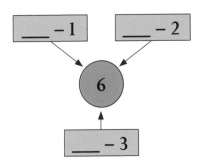

Have the students choose five different numbers from 2 to 9 for the middle. They can then write the three facts that match each number. The three facts should involve subtracting 1, 2, and 3. Confident students may like to try numbers greater than 12.

2 Write ___ + 3 = ___ on the board. Ask, What numbers between twenty and thirty could you use to make this sentence true? How do you know? Encourage the students to explain their thinking as you write their suggestions on the board. Highlight the connection between addition and subtraction by writing the related addition or subtraction fact. For example, **25 + 3 = 28** and **28 − 3 = 25**.

Repeat the activity with number sentences that involve adding 1 or 2.

3 ▶ Write **3**, **24**, and **27** on the board. Direct the students to write a fact family that involves all three numbers. Discuss the results then repeat the activity with other sets of numbers. Make sure one number in each set is 1, 2, or 3.

4 ▶ Copy and laminate Blackline Master 18. Write the numerals shown below onto the machine. Call upon individuals to provide the missing numbers and to describe the thinking they used to figure them out. Afterward, repeat the activity for other IN and OUT numbers.

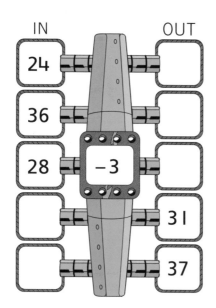

Count On 0

Introduce

Read some of the count-on-0 stories from Blackline Master 10 to the class. For each story, ask the students to describe which numbers are known, which number is unknown and how they can figure out the value of the missing quantity. Encourage the students to show their thinking using materials (e.g. counters) and to write a matching number fact. Afterward, instruct the students to write two or three stories. They can then have a partner solve their stories.

Write a number fact on the board that involves subtracting 1, 2, 3, or 0. Direct the students to use cubes of two different colors to make a cube train that shows the fact. Repeat with other facts. Include number facts that have 1, 2, 3, or 0 as the missing part.

Make laminated, blank flip cards and use a non-permanent marker to create the cards shown below.

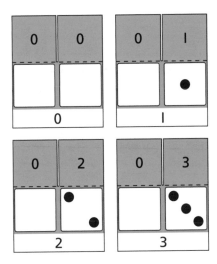

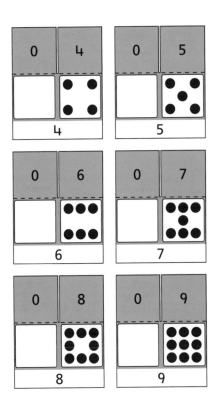

Hold the 0 + 4 card so that the flap showing 0 covers the blank panel underneath. Display the card to the students and ask, What do we know when we look at this card? (There are four dots in total and four are showing.) Are there any dots covered? How do you know? Repeat with the other cards. Use each card twice, folding a different flap each time.

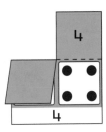

Reinforce

1 Make or select the addition flash cards shown below. Make a paper sleeve that can completely cover any symbol or numeral on the cards.

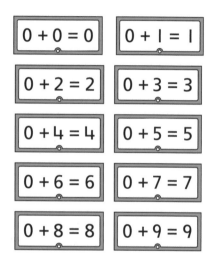

0 + 0 = 0	0 + 1 = 1
0 + 2 = 2	0 + 3 = 3
0 + 4 = 4	0 + 5 = 5
0 + 6 = 6	0 + 7 = 7
0 + 8 = 8	0 + 9 = 9

See: *Missing-Addend Subtraction Cards*

Select the 0 + 3 = 3 card and position the sleeve over the first addend as shown below. Display the card and ask, **What number is covered? How do you know?** The students should understand that when zero is added to any number, the number remains unchanged. Similarly, when zero is subtracted from any number, the number remains unchanged.

$$+ 3 = 3$$

Select another card and position the sleeve over the second addend. Display the card and ask the students to identify the missing number. Repeat with other cards as time allows, alternating between covering the first and second addends.

2 Copy Blackline Master 19 and cut out the numeral cards. Reuse the flash cards from the following activities:

- *Practice* Activity 1 on page 12
- *Practice* Activity 1 on page 18
- *Practice* Activity 1 on page 22

Select or make the double-sided flash cards shown below. The cards should be made of exactly the same paper as the flash cards used previously.

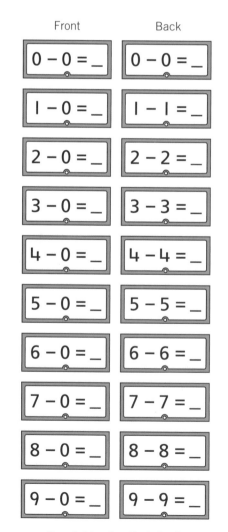

Front	Back
0 − 0 = _	0 − 0 = _
1 − 0 = _	1 − 1 = _
2 − 0 = _	2 − 2 = _
3 − 0 = _	3 − 3 = _
4 − 0 = _	4 − 4 = _
5 − 0 = _	5 − 5 = _
6 − 0 = _	6 − 6 = _
7 − 0 = _	7 − 7 = _
8 − 0 = _	8 − 8 = _
9 − 0 = _	9 − 9 = _

See: *Subtraction Flash Cards*

Display the 7 − 3 = ___ flash card with the 6 numeral card beside it. Ask, Does this make sense? Why not? Encourage the students to explain their thinking. Repeat with other pairs of matching and non-matching cards.

Give each student a copy of Blackline Master 20. Read the instruction with the students before directing them to complete the page individually.

Make an overhead transparency of Blackline Master 14. Select or make the dominoes shown below.

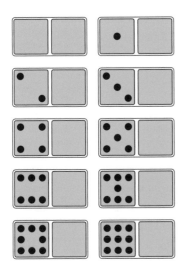

Display the domino with five and zero dots. Ask, How many dots are there in total? (Five.) How many dots are there in each part? (Five and zero.) What are two addition facts that involve these numbers? Write 5 + 0 = 5 and 0 + 5 = 5 on the transparency. Ask, What are two subtraction facts that involve all of these numbers? Write 5 − 0 = 5 and 5 − 5 = 0 on the transparency.

Afterward, erase the facts from the transparency. Repeat the activity using a different domino.

5 ▶ Write ___ − ___ = 6 on the board. Say, This is the answer to a subtraction fact. What could be the starting number? What number do you count back to get six? Encourage the students to suggest numbers that are within the range of the strategies discussed in this section. Write a number sentence for each suggestion.

Fact File
Subtracting from zero results in a negative number. Although negative numbers cannot be represented easily using hands-on materials such as counters, the concept is used in everyday situations, such as those that involve temperatures and bank statements. A number line is an ideal way of representing the relationship between negative numbers and positive numbers.

Practice

1 Reuse all the flash cards from *Reinforce* Activity 2 on page 26. Show one card and select a student to say the missing part. Allow approximately three seconds for the student to respond. Repeat several times with other students and cards (including the partner facts).

2 This is a game for two to four players. Each group will need two regular six-sided dice and a copy of Blackline Master 21. Each student will need a counter.

To play the game:

- Each player places their counter on Start.

- The first player rolls the dice.

- The player calculates the difference between the two numbers rolled and says the relevant subtraction fact aloud. The player moves their counter that number of spaces (the difference) on the game board. More than one counter can rest on a space.

- Each player takes a turn.

- The first player to reach Finish wins.

3 Give each student a copy of Blackline Master 22. Read the instruction and then have the students complete the sheet individually.

4 This activity can be completed in pairs. Each pair will need a stop watch and a set of the flash cards and numeral cards used in *Reinforce* Activity 2 on page 26. Make an extra numeral card for 0. The numeral cards should be placed in a row on the floor.

With their eyes closed, one student randomly chooses ten cards from the flash cards. When their partner starts the stop watch, they open their eyes and try to match the flash cards to the numeral cards as quickly as possible. When they are finished their partner checks that the matching is correct. Students may wish to compete against each other for fastest times, or against themselves for their "personal bests".

5 Distribute the students' record sheets used in *Practice* Activity 5 on page 13 (Blackline Master 9). Direct them to fold the sheet so that they can see only the *Count-On-0* section. This assessment task should take no more than about $1\frac{1}{2}$ minutes for the students to complete. A longer period of time may indicate that recall of the facts is not automatic. Collect the sheets afterward and record the results for each student on Blackline Masters 1 and 2. See page 5 of the *Introduction* for instructions.

Fact File
The main approach for learning the subtraction facts is to "think addition". For this reason, clusters of subtraction facts are named according to the strategy used for the related addition facts. For example, $9 - 0 = 9$ is part of the count-on subtraction fact cluster, because its related addition fact $9 + 0 = 9$ involves counting on zero.

Extend

Write **6** on the board. Read out each of the following instructions. Ask the students to write the resulting number from each instruction so that they can perform the next instruction using that number as the starting number. Say:

- Start with six.
- Subtract two.
- Subtract three.
- Add four.

Check the students answers, (the sequence 6, 4, 1, 5) then repeat with other instructions and starting numbers from 0 to 10. The instructions should involve adding any number from 0 to 9 but only subtracting 0, 1, 2, or 3. As the students become more confident, use starting numbers that are greater than 10. You may also like to challenge each student to write their own set of instructions to share with the class.

Copy and laminate Blackline Master 18. Write the numerals shown onto the machine. Challenge the students to figure out what should be written in the middle. Ask individuals to describe their thinking. Invite volunteers to provide the other missing numbers. Change the IN and OUT numbers and operations in the middle, such as +1, −1, +2, −2, +3, or −3 and repeat the activity.

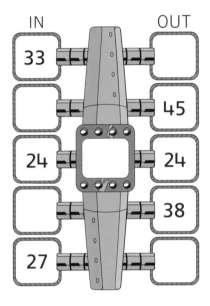

3 Make an overhead transparency from Blackline Master 23. Loop 56 and ask, If I subtract two, where will I finish? Point to 54 and say, We just subtracted two ones. Suppose I want to subtract two tens. Where will I finish? How do you know? Discuss the students' ideas before inviting a confident individual to write on the board the matching subtraction fact (56 − 20 = 36) and one or both related addition facts (20 + 36 = 56 or 36 + 20 = 56). Repeat with other numbers involving subtracting 0, 10, 20, or 30.

Use Doubles

The main approach for learning the subtraction facts is to "think addition". For this reason, clusters of subtraction facts are named according to the strategy used for the related addition facts.

The use-doubles subtraction facts are related to the use-doubles addition facts. As with the count-on facts, it is important to reinforce that these subtraction facts can be learned and recalled easily by relating them to addition.

Fact File

The use-doubles strategy is also known as the *near-doubles* strategy.

Prepare

1. Draw a number track from 1 to 20 on the board. Point to 14 and say, **This is the total for an addition fact. What fact that involves doubling, or doubling and adding two, has 14 as a total?** Discuss the students' answers. They should suggest either 7 + 7 = 14, 6 + 8 = 14, or 8 + 6 = 14. Repeat with other numbers on the track.

2. This is a game for two players. Give each pair of students a blank cube and two marker pens (a different color for each student). Have the students label the cube faces 4, 5, 6, 7, 8, and 9. The 6 and 9 should be underlined to avoid confusion. Instruct each pair to write the numerals from 8 to 18 in a row on a sheet of paper.

To play the game:

- The first player rolls the cube.

- The player can either double, double and add 1, or double and add 2 to the number shown on the cube. The player says the number fact of their choice and the other player draws a loop around the total on the sheet of paper.

- The other player has a turn to roll the cube and say the number fact.

- As the game continues, the player misses a turn if the total is already looped.

- The first player to loop three adjacent numerals wins.

3. As students participate in the activities described above, observe whether their recall is accurate and automatic. If some students are not able to easily recall the addition facts covered by the use-doubles strategy, it may be of benefit to revisit the *Use Doubles* section of *The Book of Facts: Addition*.

Double

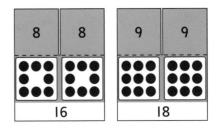

Introduce

Read some of the double stories from Blackline Master 24. For each story, ask the students to describe which numbers are known, which number is unknown and how they can figure out the value of the missing quantity. Encourage the students to explain their thinking and to write a matching number fact. Afterward, the students can write two or three stories and then have a partner solve them.

Select or make the flip cards shown below. The double-2 and double-3 cards were used previously to teach the count-on subtraction facts.

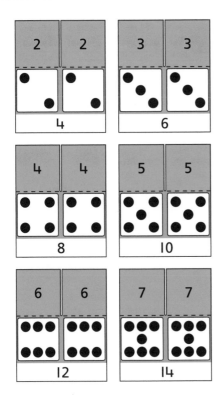

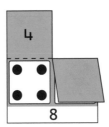

See: *Think-Addition Subtraction Strategy Cards*

Hold the double-4 card so that the right-hand flap showing 4 covers the four dots below it. Display the card to the students and ask, What do we know when we look at this card? (There are eight dots in total, but only four are showing.)

Ask, How can we figure out how many dots are covered? Highlight the link between this idea and the addition double facts. The students may use various methods to figure out the problem, but they should understand that double 4 is 8, so four dots must be covered.

Repeat the activity with the other cards. Use each card twice, folding a different flap each time. The students should conclude that each card shows two equal amounts.

3 ▶ Write **5 + 5 = 10** on the board. Show a matching domino and say the number on each side. Write other double addition facts from **0 + 0 = 0** to **9 + 9 = 18** on the board. Give each pair of students the ten doubles dominoes from a set of double-nine dominoes (see below). Instruct the students to match the dominoes to the facts on the board. Discuss the results.

Afterward, write **16 − 8 = ___** on the board. Ask, What domino can we use to figure out the missing part? How do you know? Ask a volunteer to identify the double-eight domino. Repeat with other doubles facts.

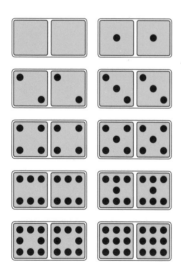

Double-nine dominoes show dots for number facts from 0 + 0 = 0 to 9 + 9 = 18. These dominoes show the doubles.

Reinforce

1 ▶ Make or select the flash cards shown below. Some of the cards will have been used previously to teach the count-on subtraction facts. Make a paper sleeve that can completely cover any symbol or numeral on the cards.

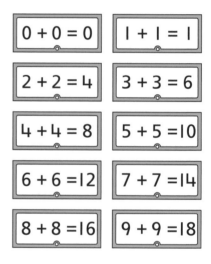

See: *Missing-Addend Subtraction Cards*

Select the 6 + 6 = 12 card and position the sleeve over the first addend. Display the card and ask, What number is covered? How do you know? The students may say, "I know that double six is twelve, so the missing number must be six."

$$\boxed{+\ 6 = 12}$$

Select another card and position the sleeve over the second addend. Display the card and ask the students to figure out the missing number. Repeat with other cards, alternating between covering the first and second addends. The students should identify that the missing number is the same regardless of which addend is covered.

2 Select or make the dominoes shown below.

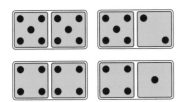

Display the domino that has five and two dots. Ask, *How many dots are there in total?* (Seven.) *How many dots are there in each part?* (Five and two.) *What addition facts involve all of these numbers?* Write **5 + 2 = 7** and **2 + 5 = 7** on the board. Ask, *What are two subtraction facts that involve all of these numbers?* Write **7 − 2 = 5** and **7 − 5 = 2** on the board. Say, *All of these facts make a fact family.* Keep the facts on the board.

Repeat the discussion with the domino showing double 5. Ask, *What do you notice about the addition facts that involve these numbers?* (They are the same: 5 + 5 = 10.) *What do you notice about the subtraction facts?* (They are the same too: 10 − 5 = 5.) *How is this different to the other domino you saw?*

Repeat the discussion with the other two dominoes shown above.

> **Fact File**
>
> The main approach for learning the subtraction facts is to "think addition". For this reason, clusters of subtraction facts are named according to the strategy used for the related addition facts. For example, 10 − 5 = 5 is part of the use-doubles subtraction fact cluster, because its related addition fact 5 + 5 = 10 involves using a double.

3 Make a copy of Blackline Master 19 and cut out the numeral cards. Select or make the double-sided flash cards shown below (the same fact is on both sides of each card). The cards should be made of exactly the same paper as the count-on cards made in previous activities.

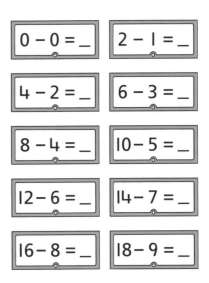

See: *Subtraction Flash Cards*

Display the flash card that shows 12 − 6 = ___ with the 4 numeral card beside it as the answer. Ask, *Does this make sense? What card will make the sentence true? How do you know?* Repeat with other cards from the set.

Practice

1 Reuse the flash cards from *Reinforce* Activity 3 on page 33. Show one card and ask a student to say the missing part and the matching addition fact. Allow approximately three seconds for the student to respond. Repeat several times with other students and cards. Count-on cards can also be used for this activity.

2 This is a game for four players. Each group will need a copy of Blackline Master 25, a blank cube, and four counters (a different color for each student). Instruct the students to label the cube 8 − 4, 10 − 5, 12 − 6, 14 − 7, 16 − 8, and 18 − 9.

To play the game:

- Each player places their counter on Start.
- The first player rolls the cube.
- The player states the difference between the two numbers and moves their counter that number of spaces on the game board. More than one counter can rest on a space.
- All the other players have a turn.
- The first player to reach Finish wins.

At a later time, the players can add extra rules or illustrate the game board.

> **Fact File**
> The word *double* comes from the Latin word *duplus*. This is a combination of *duo*, meaning "two", and *plus*, which means "fold". When something is folded over itself there are twice as many layers as before. *Two-fold* is a direct translation still used today. Examples of related words are *duplex* (a two-storey residence) and *duplicate* (to make two of something).

3 Give each student a copy of Blackline Master 26. Read the instruction and then direct the students to complete it individually.

4 This activity can be completed in pairs. Each pair will need a stop watch, a set of numeral cards from Blackline Master 19, and the flash cards used in *Reinforce* Activity 3 on page 33. Make an extra numeral card for 0. Instruct the students to place the numeral cards in a row on the floor.

With their eyes closed, one student holds the shuffled flash cards. When their partner starts the stop watch, the student opens their eyes and matches the flash cards to the numeral cards as quickly as possible. When they are finished, their partner checks that the matching is correct. The students may wish to compete against each other for fastest times, or against themselves for their "personal bests".

5 Give each student a copy of Blackline Master 27. Direct them to fold the sheet into quarters so that they can see only the *Double* section. This assessment task should take approximately one minute for the students to complete. A longer period of time may indicate that recall of the facts is not automatic. Collect the sheets afterward and record the results for each student on Blackline Masters 1 and 2. See page 5 of the *Introduction* for instructions.

Extend

Write **30 + 30 = ___** on the board. Ask, *What is double thirty? How do you know?* Write the answer and elicit several responses. For example, the students may say, "I know double three is six so double thirty must be sixty." Ask the students to identify the related subtraction fact for 60 − 30 = 30.

Write **25 + 25 = ___** on the board. Ask, *What is double twenty-five? How did you figure out the total?* Elicit several responses, for example, some students may say, "I double twenty then I double five." Ask, *What is half of fifty? What other numbers close to fifty are easy to halve?* Repeat the discussion for 35 + 35 = ___ and 45 + 45 = ___.

Write **26 = ___ + ___** on the board. Ask, *What double fact will make this sentence true? How do you know?* The students may say, "I know double ten is twenty and double three is six. So double thirteen must be twenty-six."

Repeat with other even totals between 20 and 50.

Write these number sentences on the board:

$$46 - 20 = \text{\_\_\_}$$
$$46 - 15 = \text{\_\_\_}$$
$$46 - 23 = \text{\_\_\_}$$
$$46 - 32 = \text{\_\_\_}$$

Ask, *Which sentence involves a double? How do you know?* Allow the students to talk about their ideas with a partner before discussing them as a class. For example, they may say, "I know double twenty is forty and double three is six. So the sentence that has twenty-three must be a double." Encourage the students to describe why the other sentences cannot involve doubles.

Repeat for other number sentences that have totals between 20 and 50.

Fact File

Both addition and subtraction have a part-part-total structure. In the operation of addition, two or more parts (*addends*) are joined together to form a total (*sum*). The values of the parts are known but the total is unknown.

In subtraction, the values of the total (*minuend*) and one part (*subtrahend*) are known. The value of a second part (*difference*) is unknown.

Double Plus 1

Introduce

1 Read some of the double-plus-1 stories from Blackline Master 24 to the class. For each story, ask the students to describe which numbers are known, which number is unknown and how they can figure out the value of the unknown. Encourage the students to explain their thinking and then write a matching number fact. Afterward, instruct the students to write two or three stories. They can then have a partner solve their stories.

2 Select or make the flip cards shown below. Some of the cards will have been used to teach the count-on subtraction facts.

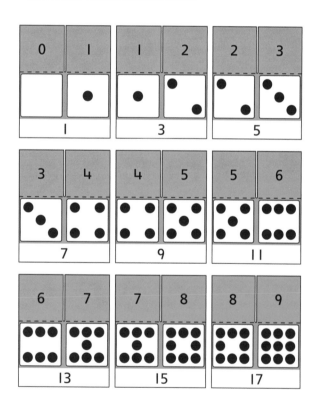

See: *Think-Addition Subtraction Strategy Cards*

Hold the 6 + 7 card so that the flap showing 7 covers the seven dots. Display the card to the students and ask, What do we know when we look at this card? (There are thirteen dots in total, but only six are visible.)

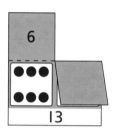

Ask, How can we figure out how many dots are covered? The students' suggestions may include, "I know that double six is twelve. One more makes thirteen, so the missing part must be seven," or, "I know that six add seven is thirteen, so seven dots must be covered." Repeat the activity with the remaining cards. Use each card twice, folding a different flap each time.

3 Write **5 + 6 = 11** on the board. Show a matching domino and say the number on each side. Ask, What is the turnaround fact? How can I show the domino for that fact? Write other double-plus-1 addition facts from **0 + 1 = 1** to **8 + 9 = 17** on the board. Instruct the students to work in pairs to find the matching domino for each fact. Discuss the results with the class.

Afterward, write **15 – 8 = ___** on the board. Ask, What domino can we use to figure out the missing part? How do you know? Ask a volunteer to identify either of the dominoes shown below. Repeat with other double-plus-1 facts.

Reinforce

Make or select the addition flash cards shown below. Some of the cards will have been used previously to teach the count-on subtraction facts. Make a paper sleeve that can completely cover any symbol or numeral on the cards.

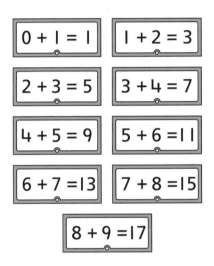

See: *Missing-Addend Subtraction Cards*

Select the 4 + 5 = 9 card and position the sleeve over the first addend as shown below. Display the card and ask, What number is covered? How do you know? You may find that some students identify the matching double-plus-1 addition fact, while others double the greater addend then subtract one. Either method is acceptable. Repeat with other cards as time allows, alternating between covering the first and second addends.

```
  +5 = 9
```

2 Ask the students to suggest addition and subtraction number sentences that involve a total of 11 as shown below and write them on the board. Ask, What patterns do you see? What number sentences are near the middle of the list? Loop the four number sentences in the middle of the lists as shown. Ask, What do you notice about the numbers in the middle of the lists? Encourage the students to describe how 5 and 6 are close to each other.

0 + 11 = 11	11 − 0 = 11
1 + 10 = 11	11 − 1 = 10
2 + 9 = 11	11 − 2 = 9
3 + 8 = 11	11 − 3 = 8
4 + 7 = 11	11 − 4 = 7
5 + 6 = 11	11 − 5 = 6
6 + 5 = 11	11 − 6 = 5
7 + 4 = 11	11 − 7 = 4
8 + 3 = 11	11 − 8 = 3
2 + 9 = 11	11 − 9 = 2
1 + 10 = 11	11 − 10 = 1
0 + 11 = 11	11 − 11 = 0

Write the first row of another two lists that involves a total of 13. Ask, Which number sentences will be near the middle of these lists? How do you know? After the students have explained their thinking, repeat the discussion for lists that involve a total of 15, 17, and 19.

3 Give each student a copy of Blackline Master 28. Read the instruction and then direct them to complete the page individually.

Practice

1 Select or make the double-sided flash cards shown below (the partner fact is on the back of each card). The cards should be made of exactly the same paper as the other flash cards used previously. Some of the count-on cards can be reused. Show one card and ask a student to say the missing number. Allow approximately three seconds for the student to respond. Repeat several times with other students and cards (including the partner facts).

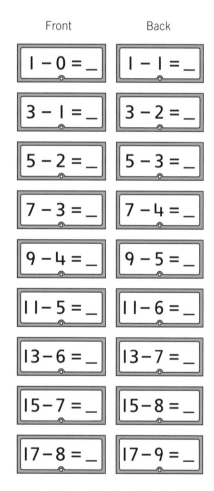

Front   Back

Front	Back
1 − 0 = _	1 − 1 = _
3 − 1 = _	3 − 2 = _
5 − 2 = _	5 − 3 = _
7 − 3 = _	7 − 4 = _
9 − 4 = _	9 − 5 = _
11− 5 = _	11− 6 = _
13− 6 = _	13− 7 = _
15− 7 = _	15− 8 = _
17− 8 = _	17− 9 = _

See: *Subtraction Flash Cards*

2 This is a game for two players. Give each student a copy of Blackline Master 29. Each student will need a spinner from Blackline Master 5, and a pencil and straightened paper clip to use with the spinner. Instruct them to label the spinner from 0 to 9 inclusive. The 6 and 9 should be underlined to avoid confusion.

To play the game:

- The first player spins the paper clip.

- The number on the spinner is an OUT number for one of the function machines. The player writes the number in a correct space on one of their three function machines.

- The other player has a turn.

- The first player to write fifteen correct OUT numbers wins.

3 Give each student a copy of Blackline Master 30. Read the instruction with the students before directing them to complete the page individually.

4 Distribute the students' record sheets used in *Practice* Activity 5 on page 34 (Blackline Master 27). Direct them to fold the sheet so that they can see only the *Double-Plus-1* section. This assessment task should take no more than about $1\frac{1}{2}$ minutes for the students to complete. A longer period of time may indicate that recall of the facts is not automatic. Collect the sheets afterward and record the results for each student on Blackline Masters 1 and 2. See page 5 of the *Introduction* for instructions.

Extend

Write **40 – 20 =** ___ on the board. Ask, *What is the missing part? How do you know?* Write **20** then say, *Add one to the total. How will you change the other numbers so that the sentence is still true?* Encourage the students to describe the possible changes. For example:

- Changing the subtrahend (41 – 21 = 20)
- Changing the difference (41 – 20 = 21)

Repeat the discussion for other number sentences such as 50 – 25 = ___ or 60 – 30 = ___.

> ### Fact File
> Both addition and subtraction have a part-part-total structure. In subtraction, the values of the total (*minuend*) and one part (*subtrahend*) are known. The value of a second part (*difference*) is unknown.
>
> $$12 \quad - \quad 7 \quad = \quad 5$$
>
> minuend   subtrahend   difference

Write **51 – 25 =** ___ on the board. Ask, *What is the missing part? How can you figure it out?* Discuss a variety of strategies. The students can use base-ten blocks to demonstrate their thinking on the overhead projector. Their suggestions may include:

- "Double twenty-five is fifty. Then add a one. That means the answer must be twenty-six."
- "Take off one. Then take half of fifty. That is twenty-five. Put back one to get twenty-six."
- "Take away half of the fifty. Twenty-five plus one is twenty-six."

Repeat the discussion for other combinations, such as 39 – 20 = ___, 49 – 25 = ___, and 81 – 40 = ___.

3 ▶ Make an overhead transparency of Blackline Master 31, or copy and laminate it. Write numerals in the diagram as shown below. Say, *The numbers shown on each "spoke" make a subtraction number sentence. Which "spoke" can you complete? How can you use the number sentences you know to figure out those you don't know?* Invite volunteers to explain how they can figure out all the missing values. Repeat with other totals from 20 to 30 inclusive.

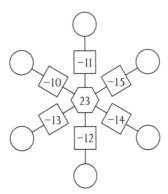

Double Plus 2

Introduce

1 Read some of the double-plus-2 stories from Blackline Master 24 to the class. For each story, ask the students to describe which numbers are known, which number is unknown and how they can figure out the missing value. Encourage the students to explain their thinking and to write a matching number fact. Afterward, instruct the students to write two or three stories. They can then have a partner solve their stories.

2 Select or make the flip cards shown below. Some of these cards will have been used to teach the count-on subtraction facts. The 0 + 2 card can be made using a blank flip card.

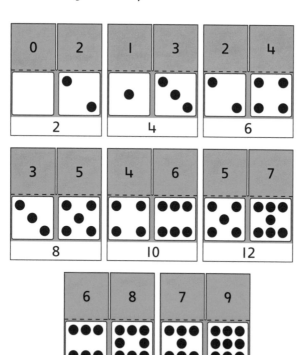

See: *Think-Addition Subtraction Strategy Cards*

Hold the 5 + 7 card so that the flap showing 7 covers the seven dots. Display the card to the students and ask, What do we know when we look at this card? (There are twelve dots in total, but only five are showing.)

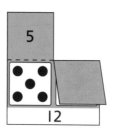

Ask, How can we figure out how many dots are covered? The students' suggestions may include, "I know that double five is ten. Two more makes twelve, so the missing part must be seven," or, "I know that five add seven is twelve, so seven dots must be covered." Repeat the activity with the other cards. Use each card twice, folding a different flap each time.

3 Write **5 + 7 = 12** on the board. Show a matching domino and say the number on each side. Ask, What is the turnaround fact? How can I show the domino for that fact? Write other double-plus-2 addition facts from 0 + 2 = 2 to 7 + 9 = 16 on the board. Instruct the students to work in pairs to find the matching domino for each fact. Discuss the results with the class.

Write **14 − 6 = ___** on the board. Ask, What domino can we use to figure out the missing value? How do you know? Choose a volunteer to identify either of the dominoes shown below. Repeat with other double-plus-2 facts.

Reinforce

Make or select the addition flash cards shown below. Some of the cards will have been used to teach the count-on subtraction facts. Make a paper sleeve that can completely cover any symbol or numeral on the cards.

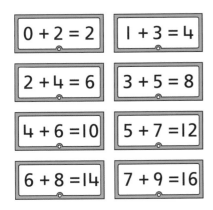

0 + 2 = 2	1 + 3 = 4
2 + 4 = 6	3 + 5 = 8
4 + 6 =10	5 + 7 =12
6 + 8 =14	7 + 9 =16

See: *Missing-Addend Subtraction Cards*

Select one card and position the sleeve over the first addend as shown. Display the card and ask, What number is covered? How do you know? You may find that some students identify the matching double-plus-2 addition fact, while others double the greater addend then subtract 2. Either method is acceptable. Repeat with other cards as time allows, alternating between covering the first and second addends.

+ 7 =12

The students can work in pairs for this activity. Give each pair two blank cubes. Instruct them to label the faces of both cubes 4, 4, 5, 5, 6, and 6. Each 6 should be underlined to avoid confusion. The numbers represent the parts that are joined together to make a total. The students take turns to roll the cubes and write the fact family for the two numbers that are rolled. The activity can be repeated using different numbers on the cubes. For example, 5, 5, 6, 6, 7, 7 or 6, 6, 7, 7, 8, 8.

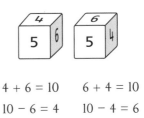

| 4 + 6 = 10 | 6 + 4 = 10 |
| 10 − 6 = 4 | 10 − 4 = 6 |

3 ▶ Read out clues for numbers that involve double-plus-2 facts, then ask the students to identify the number. For example, What number am I? If you subtract two from me and take half of that answer, you get six. Direct the students to discuss their ideas with a friend. Ask the students to share number sentences that can help them figure out the answers. For example:

$$6 + 6 + 2 = \_\_\_$$
$$\_\_\_ - 2 = 6 + 6$$

Repeat the activity with other mystery numbers. The students can also write their own puzzles that can be solved in pairs or as a whole class.

Fact File
Partner facts are pairs of subtraction facts that are related to an addition fact. For example, 12 − 9 = 3 and 12 − 3 = 9 are partner facts because they both relate to 9 + 3 = 12 and its turnaround fact 3 + 9 = 12. These four facts form a *fact family*.

Practice

1 ▷ Select or make double-sided flash cards shown below (the partner fact is on the back of each card). The cards should be made of exactly the same paper as the other flash cards used previously. Some of the count-on cards can be reused. Show one card and select a student to say the missing part. Allow approximately three seconds for the student to respond. Repeat several times with other students and cards (including the partner facts).

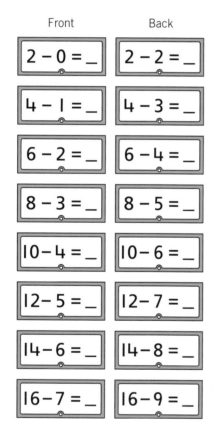

Front	Back
2 − 0 = _	2 − 2 = _
4 − 1 = _	4 − 3 = _
6 − 2 = _	6 − 4 = _
8 − 3 = _	8 − 5 = _
10 − 4 = _	10 − 6 = _
12 − 5 = _	12 − 7 = _
14 − 6 = _	14 − 8 = _
16 − 7 = _	16 − 9 = _

See: *Subtraction Flash Cards*

2 ▷ This activity can be completed in pairs. Each pair will need a stop watch, a set of the numeral cards from Blackline Master 19, and the flash cards used in the following activities:

- *Reinforce* Activity 3 on page 33
- *Practice* Activity 1 on page 38
- *Practice* Activity 1 on this page

Make an extra numeral card for 0. Instruct the students to place the numeral cards in a row on the floor.

With their eyes closed, one student randomly chooses ten flash cards. When their partner starts the stop watch, they open their eyes and try to match the flash cards to the numeral cards as quickly as possible. When they are finished their partner checks that the matching is correct. The students may wish to compete against each other for fastest times, or against themselves for their "personal bests".

3 ▷ Give each student a copy of Blackline Master 32. Read the instruction with the students and then ask them to complete the sheet individually.

4 ▷ This is a game for two players. Give each pair of students a copy of Blackline Master 33, thirty counters (15 of two different colors), and a blank cube. Instruct the students to label the faces of the cube 4, 5, 6, 7, 8, and 9. The 6 and 9 should be underlined to avoid confusion.

To play the game:

- The first player rolls the cube. The number on the cube is the answer to a subtraction fact on the game board.

- The player places a counter on a matching expression on the game board.

- The other player takes a turn.

- As the game continues, the player misses a turn if no matching space is available.

- The first player to place four adjacent counters in a 2-by-2 square or a vertical, horizontal, or diagonal line is the winner.

During the game, ask questions such as, What number do you need to roll to place a counter on that space? What do you want your next roll to be? Why?

5 ▸ Distribute the students' record sheets used in *Practice* Activity 5 on page 34 (Blackline Master 27). Direct them to fold the sheet into quarters so that they can see only the *Double-Plus-2* section. This assessment task should take approximately one minute for the students to complete. A longer period of time may indicate that recall of the facts is not automatic. Collect the sheets afterward and record the results for each student on Blackline Masters 1 and 2. See page 5 of the *Introduction* for instructions.

Extend

1 ▸ Write 20 – ___ = ___ on the board. Ask, What numbers can we add to make this sentence true? How do you know? Encourage the students to suggest numbers and write the number sentences on the board. For example, 20 – 1 = 19, 20 – 10 = 10, or 20 – 5 = 15.

After five or six sentences have been written ask, Which sentences in the list use a "double" or numbers that are close to a "double"? Loop each sentence, then ask, What are some other number sentences we can use a "double" to solve? How do you know? After several suggestions have been recorded write the following number sentences on the board:

$$20 - 10 = 10$$
$$20 - 9 = 11$$
$$20 - 11 = 9$$
$$20 - 8 = 12$$
$$20 - 12 = 8$$

Repeat the discussion for other sentences that start with a multiple of 10, such as 20, 30, or 40. As the students become more confident, use starting numbers that are easy to halve, such as 24, 32, or 48.

2 ▸ Write 24 – ___ = 11 on the board. Ask, What is the missing part? How do you know? Encourage the students to suggest a variety of strategies to figure out the missing part. For example, "I figured out the missing number by taking eleven away from twenty-four. First I took away ten and got fourteen, then I took away one more and got thirteen." Encourage the students to think of different ways that they can use a "double" to figure out the answer. The students may suggest doubling, halving, using subtraction directly, and identifying a related addition fact.

Record the thinking strategies that the students suggest on the board. Include number sentences in the descriptions. For example:

$$11 + (11 + 2) = 24$$
$$24 - 10 - 1 = 13$$
$$24 - (12 + 1) = 11$$

Afterward, repeat the discussion using these number sentences:

$$36 - \underline{} = 17$$
$$47 - \underline{} = 24$$
$$29 - \underline{} = 15$$

3 Make an overhead transparency sheet of Blackline Master 31, or copy and laminate it. Write numerals in the diagram as shown below. Say, The numbers on each "spoke" make a subtraction number sentence. Which "spoke" can you complete? How can you use the number sentence you know to help figure out those you don't know? Invite volunteers to explain how they can figure out all the missing parts. Repeat with other totals from 21 to 30 inclusive.

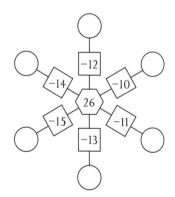

Bridge to 10

Each of these subtraction number facts is the inverse of a fact mastered by the students in the addition bridge-to-10 strategy. It is important to reinforce that these subtraction facts can be learned and recalled easily by relating them to addition.

Fact File

The bridge-to-10 strategy is also known as *bridge the decades*, *bridging across 10*, *bridging through 10*, *making 10*, *make to 10*, and *use 10*.

Prepare

1 Draw the number line shown below on the board. Underneath it, write 8 + 5 = ___.

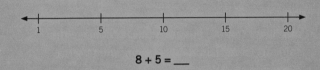

8 + 5 = ___

Ask, **What is the total for this number sentence? How do you know?** Invite volunteers to demonstrate their thinking using the number line.

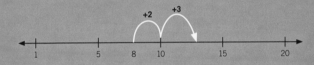

"I start at eight, count on two to get ten, then add three more to get thirteen."

Repeat with other number sentences involving 7, 8, or 9, for example, 7 + 4 = ___, 4 + 8 = ___, and 9 + 6 = ___.

2 Give each pair of students two blank cubes. Instruct them to write the numerals 9, 9, 8, 8, 7, and 7 on one cube and 4, 4, 5, 5, 6, and 6 on the other cube. Each 6 and 9 should be underlined to avoid confusion. Direct each pair of students to roll the cubes and record the two numerals shown. Have them write a number fact involving the two numbers and a bridge-to-10 fact that they can use to figure out the answer. The students may choose to record more than one fact. Repeat as time allows.

3 Observe the students as they complete *Prepare* Activities 1 and 2 to check that their recall is accurate and automatic. If some students are not able to easily recall the addition facts covered by the bridge-to-10 strategy, revisit activities from the *Bridge-to-10* section of *The Book of Facts: Addition*.

Introduce

1 ▶ Read some of the bridge-to-10 stories from Blackline Master 24 to the class. For each story, ask the students to describe which numbers are known, which number is unknown and how they can figure out the missing value. Encourage the students to explain their thinking and to write a matching number fact. Afterward, instruct the students to write two or three stories. They can then have a partner solve their stories.

2 ▶ Write 17 – ___ = ___ on the board. Ask, What numbers make this sentence true? How do you know? Encourage the students to say all of the sentences they know. Write the sentences on the board as the students explain their thinking. Ask, Which number sentences have both missing numbers close to ten? Loop the sentences that the students say.

$$17 - 0 = 17$$
$$17 - 1 = 16$$
$$17 - 2 = 15$$
$$17 - 3 = 14$$
$$...$$
$$17 - 17 = 0$$

Repeat the activity for other number sentences with answers ranging from 13 to 19.

3 ▶ Select or make the flip cards shown. The students will have encountered many other flip cards involving 7, 8, and 9, so this activity concentrates on the remaining facts involving these amounts.

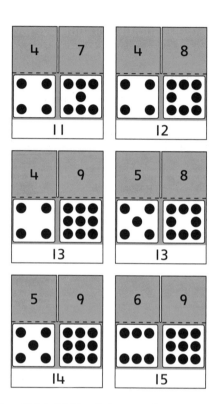

See: *Think-Addition Subtraction Strategy Cards*

Hold the 4 + 9 card so that the flap showing 9 covers the nine dots. Display the card to the students and ask, What do we know when we look at this card? (There are thirteen dots in total, but only four are showing.)

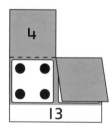

Ask, How can we figure out how many dots are covered? Discuss the students' suggestions and encourage them to think addition. Repeat the activity with the other cards. Use each card twice, folding a different flap each time.

Reinforce

1 Make or select the addition flash cards shown below. Make a paper sleeve that can completely cover any symbol or numeral on the cards.

$$4 + 7 = 11 \qquad 4 + 8 = 12$$

$$4 + 9 = 13 \qquad 5 + 8 = 13$$

$$5 + 9 = 14 \qquad 6 + 9 = 15$$

See: *Missing-Addend Subtraction Cards*

Select the 4 + 7 = 11 card and position the sleeve over the first addend as shown below. Display the card and ask, **What number is covered? How do you know?** Some students may think of the matching bridge-to-10 addition fact, while others count back to 10 then count back to 7. Repeat with other cards as time allows, alternating between covering the first and second addends.

$$[\ ] + 7 = 11$$

2 Write this number sentence on the board.

$$16 - \boxed{8} = \boxed{8}$$

Ask, **How can you change the numbers in the boxes so the starting number is always the same?** Demonstrate that when one value increases, the other value must decrease. Write the students' suggestions on the board. For example:

$$16 - 10 = 6$$
$$16 - 9 = 7$$
$$16 - 8 = 8$$
$$16 - 7 = 9$$
$$16 - 6 = 10$$

Ask, **How did you figure out what numbers worked? What patterns do you see?** Repeat the activity with other starting numbers between 12 and 18.

3 Make an overhead transparency of Blackline Master 31, or copy and laminate it. Write numerals in the diagram as shown below. Say, **The numbers on each "spoke" make a subtraction number sentence. Which number sentences do you know how to complete? How can you use this information to figure out the number sentences you do not know?** Invite volunteers to explain how they figured out the missing values. Repeat with other totals from 11 to 20 inclusive.

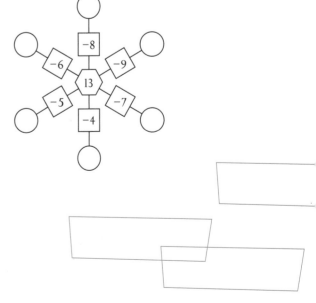

Fact File

A *number* is used for counting, labeling, and ordering.

A *numeral* is the symbol used to represent a number.

An *expression* is a combination of numerals and operation symbols (e.g. 16 – 1).

A *number sentence* is a statement of the relationship between two or more expressions (e.g. 16 – 1 = 15).

4 ▶ The students can work in pairs for this activity. Give each pair two blank cubes. Instruct the students to label the faces of one cube 4, 4, 5, 5, 6, and 6 and the faces of the other cube 7, 7, 8, 8, 9, and 9. Each 6 and 9 should be underlined to avoid confusion. The numbers represent the parts that are joined together to make a total. The students take turns to roll the cubes and write the fact family for the two numbers that are rolled. For example, if 4 and 8 are rolled, the fact family is:

$$8 + 4 = 12 \qquad 4 + 8 = 12$$
$$12 - 4 = 8 \qquad 12 - 8 = 4$$

Fact File

The main approach for learning the subtraction facts is to "think addition". For this reason, clusters of subtraction facts are named according to the strategy used for the related addition facts. For example, 14 – 5 = 9 is part of the bridge-to-10 subtraction fact cluster, because its related addition fact 9 + 5 = 14 involves bridging to 10.

Practice

1 ▶ Select or make the double-sided flash cards shown below (the partner fact is on the back of each card). The cards should be made of exactly the same paper as all other flash cards used previously. Some of the count-on cards can be reused. Show one card and select a student to say the missing part. Allow approximately three seconds for the student to respond. Repeat several times with other students and cards (including the partner facts).

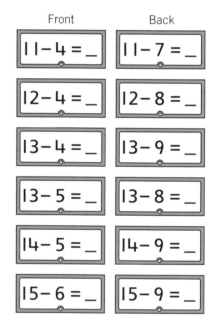

See: *Subtraction Flash Cards*

2 ▶ Give each student a copy of Blackline Master 34. Ensure that the students understand the instruction and then allow them time to complete the sheet individually.

3 ▶ This is a game for two players. The students can reuse the cube labeled 7, 7, 8, 8, 9, and 9 from *Reinforce* Activity 4 on page 48. Give each pair a blank cube, a copy of Blackline Master 35, and twenty counters (ten of two different colors). Instruct them to label the faces of the blank cube 10, 11, 12, 13, 14, and 15.

To play the game:

- The first player rolls both cubes.

- The player calculates the difference between the two numbers rolled and places a counter on a matching answer on the game board.

- The other player has a turn.

- The first player to make a vertical, horizontal or diagonal line of three adjacent counters wins.

During the game, ask questions such as, What number do you need to roll to place a counter on that space? What do you hope your next roll is? Why?

4 ▶ Distribute the students' record sheets from *Practice* Activity 5 on page 34 (Blackline Master 27). Direct them to fold the sheet into quarters so that they can see only the *Bridge-to-10* section. This assessment task should take approximately $1\frac{1}{2}$ minutes for the students to complete. A longer period of time may indicate that recall of the facts is not automatic. Collect the sheets afterward and record the results for each student on Blackline Masters 1 and 2. See page 5 of the *Introduction* for instructions.

Extend

1 ▶ Write **14 − 8 = ___** on the board. Say, Imagine that you add a small number to fourteen. What will you need to do to eight to make the missing part stay the same? How do you know the answer will be the same? The students could demonstrate their thinking on a number line. Repeat the discussion with other numbers as time allows.

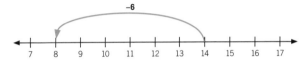

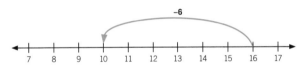

"If I add two to fourteen I need to add two to eight so that the gap stays the same."

2 ▶ Write on the board:

$$\square - 9 = \bigcirc$$

Ask, What number can you put in the square so that the number in the circle is more than ten? Encourage the students to suggest numbers they find easy to use. For example:

$$\boxed{29} - 9 = \bigcirc$$

$$\boxed{39} - 9 = \bigcirc$$

$$\boxed{28} - 9 = \bigcirc$$

After a number is suggested, encourage several students to explain different strategies for figuring out the number in the circle. Write each sentence on the board as it is suggested.

Fact File

Both addition and subtraction have a part-part-total structure. In subtraction, the values of the total (*minuend*) and one part (*subtrahend*) are known. The value of the second part (*difference*) is unknown.

$$12 \quad - \quad 7 \quad = \quad 5$$

minuend   subtrahend   difference

---

3   Write these number sentences on the board:

$$15 - 9 = \underline{\quad}$$
$$25 - 9 = \underline{\quad}$$
$$35 - 9 = \underline{\quad}$$
$$45 - 9 = \underline{\quad}$$
$$55 - 9 = \underline{\quad}$$

Ask, Which sentences can you complete? How do you know what the missing values are? How can they help you figure out other missing values? When all of the answers have been recorded ask, What patterns do you notice?

Write these number sentences beside the first set:

$$16 - 9 = \underline{\quad}$$
$$26 - 9 = \underline{\quad}$$
$$36 - 9 = \underline{\quad}$$
$$46 - 9 = \underline{\quad}$$
$$56 - 9 = \underline{\quad}$$

Ask, How can you figure out the missing values? Encourage the students to explain a range of strategies they can use. They may use answers in either the right or the left column. Repeat the activity using other totals and a subtrahend of 9. Repeat the entire activity at a later time using a subtrahend of 8.

4   Draw a number line and arrow as shown below. Ask, What subtraction sentence can we write to figure out the length of the number line between the beginning and the end of the arrow? How can we use this sentence to figure out the answer? Highlight that the length is the difference between the two numbers. Write $25 - 19 = \underline{\quad}$ on the board.

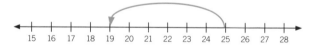

Ask, Where can I draw an arrow that has the same length? How do you know? Encourage the students to use the first arrow to help them decide where to draw the second arrow. Repeat the activity as time allows.

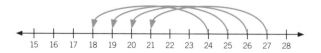

All the Facts

The activities in this section are designed to help the students revisit their knowledge of all the basic subtraction facts and the count-on, use-doubles, and bridge-to-10 strategies. Therefore, the activities begin with reinforcing what the students know. In this section, the students use all of the subtraction flash cards they have used previously. Compile a complete set of subtraction flash cards from these activities:

Practice Activity 1, page 12
Practice Activity 1, page 18
Practice Activity 1, page 22
Reinforce Activity 2, page 26
Reinforce Activity 3, page 33
Practice Activity 1, page 38
Practice Activity 1, page 42
Practice Activity 1, page 48

Collate a complete set of flip cards from these activities:

Introduce Activity 3, page 10
Introduce Activity 5, page 16
Introduce Activity 3, page 20
Introduce Activity 3, page 25
Introduce Activity 2, page 31
Introduce Activity 2, page 36
Introduce Activity 2, page 40
Introduce Activity 3, page 46

Reinforce

1 Outside class time, look through the tracking sheet and number fact grids that have been used to record the facts the students know (Blackline Masters 1 and 2). If most students seem to know all the basic facts, ask them during class time to write five facts that they find the easiest and five facts they find the most difficult. This will give some indication of the activities in the book that require revision.

Facts Grid

Name: _____

Find the total in the left-hand column. Then find the known part in the top row.

Known Fact

−	0	1	2	3	4	5	6	7	8	9
0	0										
1	1	0									
2	2	1	0								
3	3	2	1	0							
4	4	3	2	1	0						
5	5	4	3	2	1	0					
6	6	5	4	3	2	1	0				
7	7	6	5	4	3	2	1	0			
8	8	7	6	5	4	3	2	1	0		
9	9	8	7	6	5	4	3	2	1	0	
10		9	8	7	6	5	4	3	2	1	
11			9	8	7	6	5	4	3	2	
12				9	8	7	6	5	4	3	
13					9	8	7	6	5	4	
14						9	8	7	6	5	
15							9	8	7	6	
16								9	8	7	
17									9	8	
18										9	

Total

Blackline Master 1

THE BOOK OF FACTS • SUBTRACTION

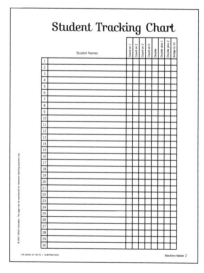

Student Tracking Chart

Student Names

THE BOOK OF FACTS • SUBTRACTION

Blackline Master 2

2 Select a flip card and hold it so that both flaps cover the dots. Display the card and ask, What two numbers give this total? Then unfold one flap and ask, What must the missing part be? How do you know? Repeat with other flip cards.

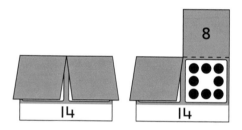

3 Direct each student to write ten addition facts from 0 + 0 = 0 to 9 + 9 = 18. They should not include turnaround facts.

Shuffle the subtraction flash cards then select the top card and read out the number sentence it shows. Instruct the students to search for a related addition fact in their lists. If a student has one of the facts they draw a ✓ next to that fact. Call on two volunteers to state the related addition facts and then repeat the activity. When a student has five ✓, they call out "Bingo" to win.

4 Give each student a copy of Blackline Master 36. Read the stories to the class and then allow time for the students to complete the page individually.

5 Have the students write their own stories to match given subtraction facts. Use facts from a range of subtraction strategies. Afterward, call upon volunteers to read their stories and discuss whether the stories match the facts. At a later time the students can write some stories using facts they choose themselves, then give their stories to a partner to solve.

Practice

For this activity, the students can work in small groups to invent their own game that uses the subtraction flash cards. They can use a copy of Blackline Master 25 as a game board or draw their own. Direct the students to discuss the game rules and then write them on a separate sheet of paper. A sample set of the game rules are shown below.

To play the game:

- All the counters begin on Start.
- All the flash cards are shuffled and placed in a stack.
- The first player selects the top card and identifies the missing part. If they are correct they move their counter ahead that number of spaces. If they are incorrect they miss a turn.
- Each of the other players takes a turn.
- The first player to reach Finish wins.

2 This is a game for three players. Make two sets of numeral cards from Blackline Master 19 for each group. Instruct the students to shuffle the cards.

To play the game:

- Two of the players sit facing one another with the cards placed facedown in a stack between them.
- Each of the two players draws a card and without looking at it, holds their card face out.
- The third player adds the two numbers and says the total.
- Each player uses the total and what can be seen on the other player's card to figure out the value that is shown on their own card.

- When all the cards have been used, they are returned to the stack and re-shuffled.
- The players switch roles and repeat the game.

As students finish a round, encourage them to describe how they figured out the value of their own card.

3 This is a game for three players. Each group will need ten subtraction flash cards and forty counters (twenty each of two different colors). One student is an umpire and has all the counters at the start of the game.

To play the game:

- Keeping the stack of cards hidden, the umpire selects the top card from the stack and reads out the number sentence it shows.
- The first player to say the missing part is awarded a counter by the umpire. If a player answers incorrectly the umpire takes a counter from the player. If both players answer correctly at the same time, both receive a counter.
- The umpire continues until all the counters have been distributed.
- If all the cards are used, they are re-shuffled, and play continues.
- The player (not including the umpire) with the most counters at the end of the game wins.

Instruct the students to change positions after each game and to shuffle the cards. After three games, direct the groups to exchange cards.

4 This is a game for two players. Each pair will need a calculator and ten subtraction flash cards.

To play the game:

- The cards are shuffled and shared equally between the two players.

- At the starting time, each player selects the top card from their stack. One player mentally calculates the missing value on their card. The other player uses the calculator to figure out the missing value on their card. Both players record their results.

- As a card is completed, it is placed facedown beside the player. The next card is then selected.

- The first player to complete their stack of cards earns three points.

- Once both players have completed their cards, they check their answers together. Each correct answer earns one bonus point.

- The player with the greatest score is the winner.

Instruct the students to change roles after each game. After two games, direct the groups to exchange cards.

5 Give each student a copy of Blackline Master 37. Ensure that the students understand the instruction and then ask them to complete the sheet individually.

Extend

1 Make an overhead transparency of Blackline Master 23. Use the number board to discuss ways of subtracting numbers that are a slightly less than a multiple of 10. For example, point to 56 and ask, What number is nine less? Nineteen less? Twenty-nine less? Thirty-nine less? Invite a volunteer to loop each answer and ask them to explain the pattern they see. Ask, How did you know what number to loop? The student may say, "Subtracting nine is the same as subtracting ten then adding one. To subtract nineteen I subtracted twenty and added one."

11	12	13	14	15	16	17	18	19	20
21	22	23	24	25	26	27	28	29	30
31	32	33	34	35	36	37	38	39	40
41	42	43	44	45	46	47	48	49	50
51	52	53	54	55	56	57	58	59	60
61	62	63	64	65	66	67	68	69	70

Encourage the class to discuss other methods for subtracting 9 and 19. For example, they could add 1 and then subtract 10. Repeat this discussion with other starting numbers such as 74, 49, and 61.

2 Repeat the previous activity using subtrahends that are a slightly greater than a multiple of 10. For example, start with 65 and subtract 12, 22, 32, and so on. Ensure that the students explain the pattern and their thinking as they place the counters.

This model helps to explain a natural method for mentally subtracting. For example, to subtract 12 from 65 many people move the counter one row back and left two spaces. In this way, the "tens" are subtracted first. Another method is to move the counter two spaces to the left then back one row. In this method, the "ones" are subtracted first as they are in the traditional algorithm.

The students may use the count-on, use-doubles, or bridge-to-10 strategies (or invent other strategies) to work with numbers other than those included in the basic facts. Using blank number lines is a useful way of showing the reference numbers students prefer to work with and the strategies they use.

Write **24 − 8 =** ___ on the board. Draw an unmarked line on the board and say, This is a number line. We only write the numbers that we need to figure out the answer on this number line. What numbers should we mark on it to solve 24 − 8 = ___? Allow the students time to discuss the answer with a friend. Ask a confident individual to explain and demonstrate their approach. For example, they may say, "I would mark twenty-four first because that is the total. Then I jump back four to twenty, then four more to sixteen." Ask the students to share and demonstrate different approaches. Repeat with other number sentences that involve two-digit numerals.

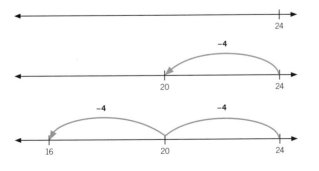

Facts Grid

Name: _____

Find the total in the left-hand column. Then find the known part in the top row.

Known Fact

−	0	1	2	3	4	5	6	7	8	9
0	0									
1	1	0								
2	2	1	0							
3	3	2	1	0						
4	4	3	2	1	0					
5	5	4	3	2	1	0				
6	6	5	4	3	2	1	0			
7	7	6	5	4	3	2	1	0		
8	8	7	6	5	4	3	2	1	0	
9	9	8	7	6	5	4	3	2	1	0
10		9	8	7	6	5	4	3	2	1
11			9	8	7	6	5	4	3	2
12				9	8	7	6	5	4	3
13					9	8	7	6	5	4
14						9	8	7	6	5
15							9	8	7	6
16								9	8	7
17									9	8
18										9

Total

Student Tracking Chart

	Student Names	Count on 1	Count on 2	Count on 3	Count on 0	Double	Double plus 1	Double plus 2	Bridge to 10
1									
2									
3									
4									
5									
6									
7									
8									
9									
10									
11									
12									
13									
14									
15									
16									
17									
18									
19									
20									
21									
22									
23									
24									
25									
26									
27									
28									
29									
30									

Flip Cards

Name: _____

Write an addition fact and a subtraction fact for each picture.

a. 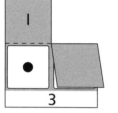 _____ + _____ = _____ _____ − _____ = _____	**b.** 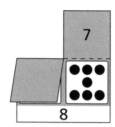 _____ + _____ = _____ _____ − _____ = _____
c. 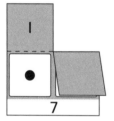 _____ + _____ = _____ _____ − _____ = _____	**d.** 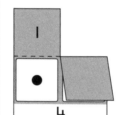 _____ + _____ = _____ _____ − _____ = _____
e. 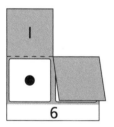 _____ + _____ = _____ _____ − _____ = _____	**f.** 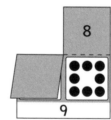 _____ + _____ = _____ _____ − _____ = _____
g. 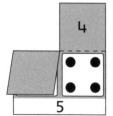 _____ + _____ = _____ _____ − _____ = _____	**h.** 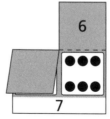 _____ + _____ = _____ _____ − _____ = _____

Domino Match

Name: _____

Draw the missing dots and complete the addition fact.
Then write 2 related subtraction facts.

a. | 6 + ____ = 7 | 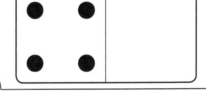 | 7 - 6 = ____
| | | 7 - 1 = ____

b. | 4 + ____ = 5 | 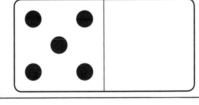 | ____ - ____ = ____
| | | ____ - ____ = ____

c. | 5 + ____ = 6 | | ____ - ____ = ____
| | | ____ - ____ = ____

d. | ____ + 7 = 8 | 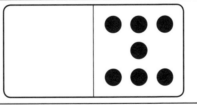 | ____ - ____ = ____
| | | ____ - ____ = ____

e. | 9 + ____ = 10 | 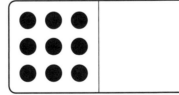 | ____ - ____ = ____
| | | ____ - ____ = ____

f. | ____ + 3 = 4 | 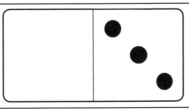 | ____ - ____ = ____
| | | ____ - ____ = ____

Blank Spinners

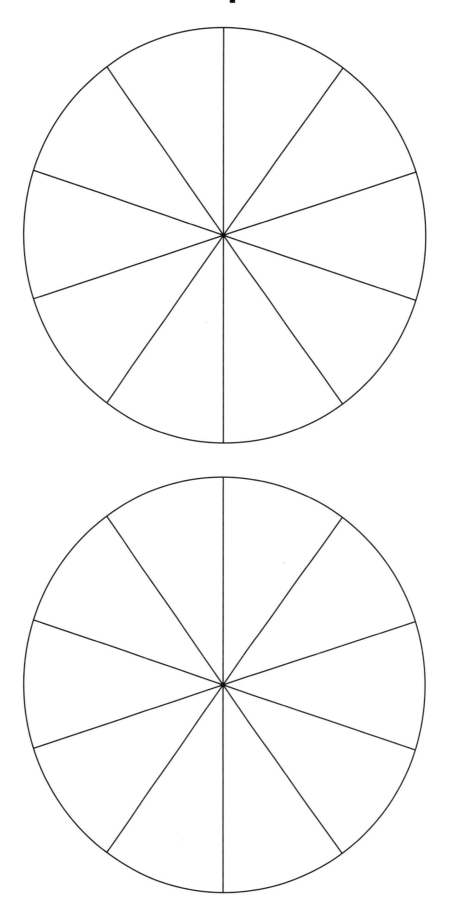

Count-on Cover-ups

3 – 1	4 – 1	4 – 3	6 – 1
6 – 5	3 – 2	5 – 1	7 – 6
7 – 6	4 – 1	7 – 1	5 – 4
6 – 1	5 – 4	5 – 1	3 – 2

6 – 5	9 – 8	10 – 9	9 – 1
8 – 1	7 – 1	6 – 1	8 – 7
10 – 1	7 – 6	9 – 1	6 – 5
9 – 8	8 – 7	8 – 1	7 – 1

More Count-on Cover-ups

1 + ___ = 3	___ + 1 = 4	3 + ___ = 4	1 + ___ = 6
___ + 5 = 6	___ + 2 = 3	1 + ___ = 5	___ + 6 = 7
6 + ___ = 7	1 + ___ = 4	___ + 1 = 7	4 + ___ = 5
___ + 1 = 6	4 + ___ = 5	1 + ___ = 5	2 + ___ = 3

5 + ___ = 6	___ + 8 = 9	9 + ___ = 10	___ + 1 = 9
1 + ___ = 8	___ + 1 = 7	1 + ___ = 6	7 + ___ = 8
___ + 1 = 10	6 + ___ = 7	___ + 1 = 9	___ + 5 = 6
8 + ___ = 9	___ + 7 = 8	1 + ___ = 8	1 + ___ = 7

Crunchy Count-ons

Name: _____

Complete each number fact.

a. $2-1 =$ _____

b. $10-9 =$ _____

c. $6-1 =$ _____

d. $8-1 =$ _____

e. $4-3 =$ _____

f. $7-6 =$ _____

g. $9-1 =$ _____

h. $4-1 =$ _____

i. $5-4 =$ _____

j. $3-1 =$ _____

k. $8-7 =$ _____

l. $9-8 =$ _____

m. $6-5 =$ _____

n. $10-1 =$ _____

o. $7-1 =$ _____

p. $5-1 =$ _____

q. $3-2 =$ _____

Count on 1

Write the answers as fast as you can.

$2 - 1 = $ ___ $6 - 5 = $ ___ $4 - 1 = $ ___

$4 - 3 = $ ___ $10 - 1 = $ ___ $10 - 9 = $ ___

$7 - 1 = $ ___ $3 - 1 = $ ___ $6 - 1 = $ ___

$9 - 8 = $ ___ $5 - 4 = $ ___ $7 - 6 = $ ___

$5 - 1 = $ ___ $8 - 7 = $ ___ $9 - 1 = $ ___

$8 - 1 = $ ___ $3 - 2 = $ ___

Count on 2

Write the answers as fast as you can.

$5 - 2 = $ ___ $7 - 2 = $ ___ $11 - 2 = $ ___

$8 - 6 = $ ___ $10 - 2 = $ ___ $6 - 2 = $ ___

$9 - 2 = $ ___ $5 - 3 = $ ___ $9 - 7 = $ ___

$11 - 9 = $ ___ $8 - 2 = $ ___

$6 - 4 = $ ___ $7 - 5 = $ ___

$4 - 2 = $ ___ $10 - 8 = $ ___

Count on 3

Write the answers as fast as you can.

$6 - 3 = $ ___ $12 - 9 = $ ___

$10 - 7 = $ ___ $7 - 3 = $ ___

$8 - 3 = $ ___ $11 - 3 = $ ___

$12 - 3 = $ ___ $9 - 6 = $ ___

$7 - 4 = $ ___ $10 - 3 = $ ___

$9 - 3 = $ ___ $8 - 5 = $ ___

$11 - 8 = $ ___

Count on 0

Write the answers as fast as you can.

$8 - 0 = $ ___ $9 - 9 = $ ___ $0 - 0 = $ ___

$1 - 1 = $ ___ $5 - 5 = $ ___ $9 - 0 = $ ___

$6 - 6 = $ ___ $1 - 0 = $ ___ $6 - 0 = $ ___

$2 - 0 = $ ___ $3 - 0 = $ ___ $7 - 7 = $ ___

$3 - 3 = $ ___ $5 - 0 = $ ___ $2 - 2 = $ ___

$7 - 0 = $ ___ $8 - 8 = $ ___

$4 - 0 = $ ___ $4 - 4 = $ ___

Count on 1

I have 8 buttons on my shirt. If 1 falls off, how many will be left?

Lucy was given 2 dolls as a present. She unwrapped another present. Now she has 3 dolls. How many extra dolls did she receive?

Matthew's team needs 5 points to win the game. They have scored 1 point. How many more points do they need to win the game?

There were 6 cookies on a plate, then 5 were eaten. How many cookies are left?

There are 7 fish in a tank. Only 6 can be seen. How many fish are hiding?

Sarah has read 2 books this week. She wants to read 3 books. How many more books must she read?

Count on 2

My friend bought 8 apples. We ate 2 of them. How many apples are left?

David had 4 marbles. Eddie gave David some more marbles. David now has 6 marbles. How many marbles did Eddie give David?

Yesterday the chickens laid 7 eggs. Today they laid 9 eggs. How many more eggs did they lay today than yesterday?

Amber caught 8 fish. Tony caught 2 fish. How many more fish did Amber catch than Tony?

We bought 5 tomatoes. We used 3 of them to make a salad. How many tomatoes do we have left?

Jessica had 6 trading cards. She gave some to her friends. She now has 2 trading cards. How many cards did she give away?

Count on 3

There were 5 birds sitting on a fence then 3 flew away. How many birds are on the fence now?

There are 11 fish in a tank. Some are hiding but 3 can be seen. How many are hiding?

Jack can invite 8 friends to his party. He has invited 3 friends already. How many more friends can he invite?

There were 12 bags on the floor. The students picked up 9 of them. How many bags are still on the floor?

Emily had 2 balloons. Sophie gave her some more. Emily now has 5 balloons. How many balloons did Sophie give Emily?

Michael has 4 trading cards. Jacob has 7 trading cards. How many more cards does Jacob have than Michael?

Count on 0

Lucy has 5 dolls. She does not give any to her sister. How many dolls does Lucy have?

There were 4 frogs in the pond. None of them jumped out. How many frogs are in the pond now?

Emma has 6 fish. Chris has no fish. How many more fish does Emma have than Chris?

I had 8 jelly beans. I ate all of them. How many do I have left?

There were 5 books on the table. I put them on the shelf. How many books are left on the table?

Tony has 3 marbles and Sarah has 3 marbles. How many more marbles does Sarah have than Tony?

Story Match-up

Name: _____

Draw a line to connect each story to its matching number fact.

a.

Kayla had 9 lollipops. She gave 2 to Michael. How many lollipops does Kayla have left?

$4-2=$ ____

b.

Jack's cat has 5 kittens. There are 4 female kittens. How many are males?

$7-5=$ ____

c.

Ashley can have 6 friends at her party. She has invited 5 friends already. How many more friends can she invite?

$9-2=$ ____

d.

There were 11 people on a bus and 9 of them got off. How many people were left on the bus?

$5-4=$ ____

e.

There were 5 balls in the box. More balls are put in. There are now 7 balls in total. How many extra balls were put in the box?

$11-9=$ ____

f.

James has 2 toy cars. He wants to own 4 in total. How many more cars does he need to buy?

$6-5=$ ____

Hat Facts

Name: _____

Complete each number fact.

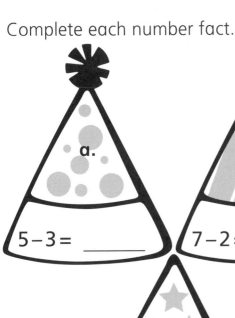
a. $5-3=$ _____

b. $7-2=$ _____

c. $4-2=$ _____

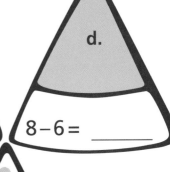
d. $8-6=$ _____

e. $10-2=$ _____

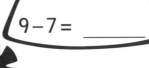
f. $11-9=$ _____

g. $9-7=$ _____

h. $6-4=$ _____

i. $5-2=$ _____

j. $8-2=$ _____

k. $7-5=$ _____

l. $11-2=$ _____

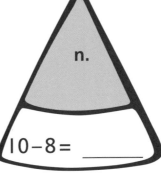
m. $9-2=$ _____

n. $10-8=$ _____

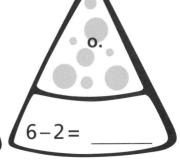
o. $6-2=$ _____

Line Up

10	6	9	7
6	9	5	8
5	7	8	10
6	8	9	7

1	2	1	2
2	1	2	1
1	2	1	2
2	1	2	1

Fact Family

Fact Families

Name: _____

Write the fact family for each domino.

a.

$3 + 5 =$ ____ $5 + 3 =$ ____

$8 - 3 =$ ____ $8 - 5 =$ ____

b.

$7 + 3 =$ ____ $3 + 7 =$ ____

____ $- 7 =$ ____   ____ $- 3 =$ ____

c.

____ $+$ ____ $=$ ____   ____ $+$ ____ $=$ ____

____ $-$ ____ $=$ ____   ____ $-$ ____ $=$ ____

d.

____ $+$ ____ $=$ ____   ____ $+$ ____ $=$ ____

____ $-$ ____ $=$ ____   ____ $-$ ____ $=$ ____

e.

____ $+$ ____ $=$ ____   ____ $+$ ____ $=$ ____

____ $-$ ____ $=$ ____   ____ $-$ ____ $=$ ____

f.

____ $+$ ____ $=$ ____   ____ $+$ ____ $=$ ____

____ $-$ ____ $=$ ____   ____ $-$ ____ $=$ ____

1, 2, 3 Function Machine

Name: _____

Write the missing numbers for each machine.

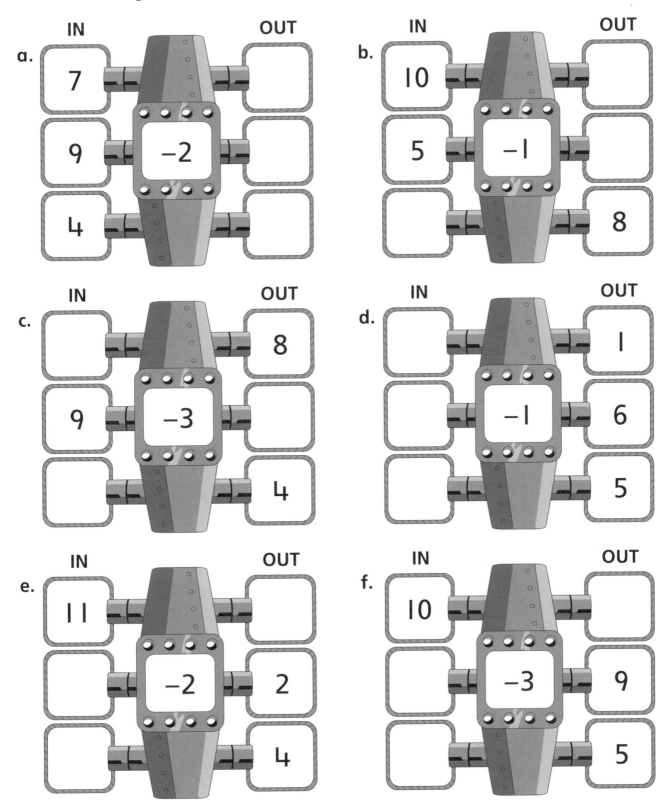

Bubbles

Name: _____

Complete each number fact.

a. $6 - 3 =$ _____

b. $9 - 6 =$ _____

c. $10 - 3 =$ _____

d. $8 - 3 =$ _____

e. $12 - 9 =$ _____

f. $11 - 3 =$ _____

g. $7 - 4 =$ _____

h. $11 - 8 =$ _____

i. $10 - 7 =$ _____

j. $9 - 3 =$ _____

k. $12 - 3 =$ _____

l. $7 - 3 =$ _____

m. $8 - 5 =$ _____

Function Machine

IN

OUT

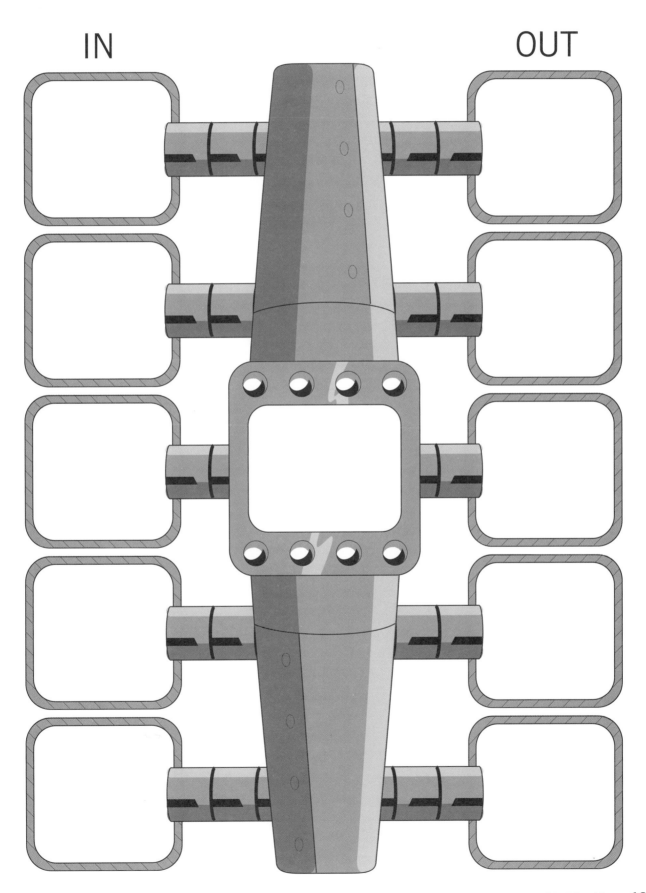

Numeral Cards 1 to 9

1	2	3
4	5	<u>6</u>
7	8	<u>9</u>

Count-on Function Machine

Name: _____

Write the missing numbers for each machine.

a.
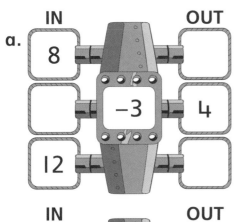

b.
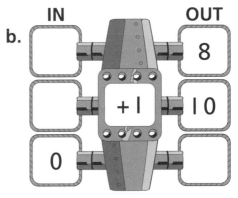

c.
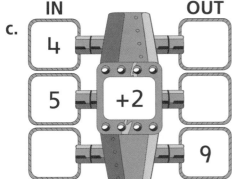

d.
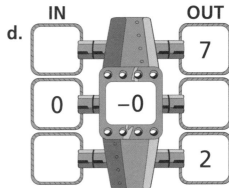

e.
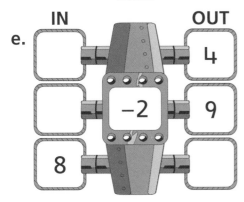

f.
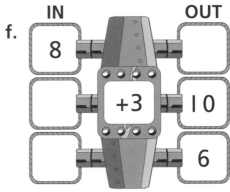

g.
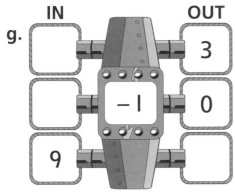

h.
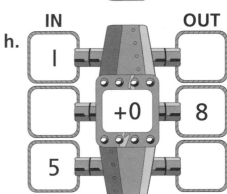

Trampolines

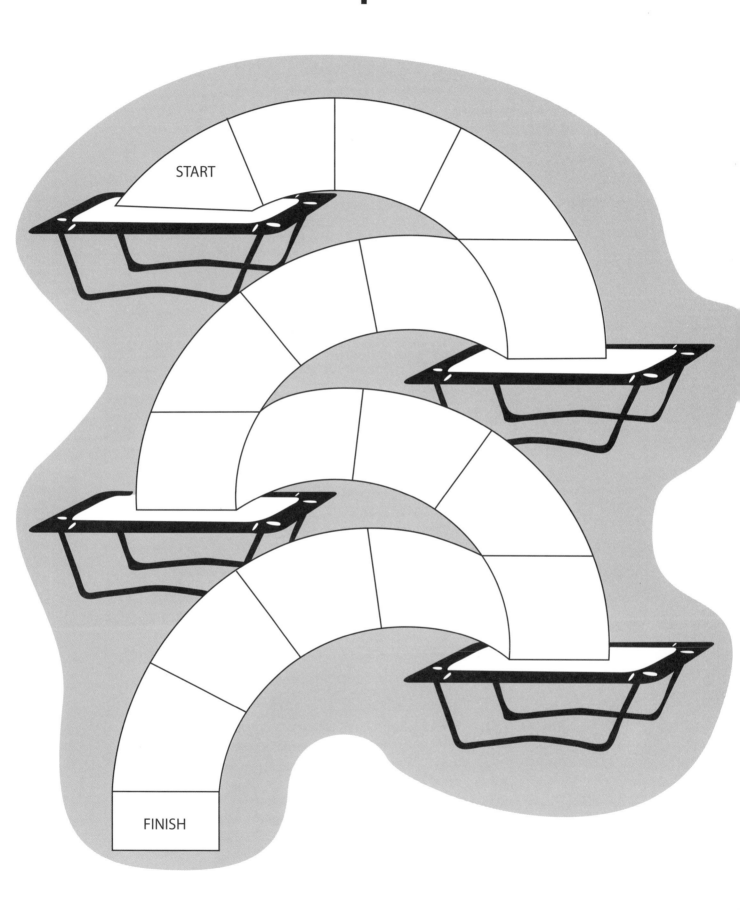

START

FINISH

Count-on Jelly Beans

Name: _____

Complete each number fact.

a. $6 - 6 =$ _____

b. $3 - 0 =$ _____

c. $7 - 0 =$ _____

d. $9 - 9 =$ _____

e. $2 - 0 =$ _____

f. $1 - 1 =$ _____

g. $5 - 5 =$ _____

h. $4 - 0 =$ _____

i. $8 - 8 =$ _____

j. $7 - 7 =$ _____

k. $9 - 0 =$ _____

l. $6 - 0 =$ _____

m. $1 - 0 =$ _____

n. $4 - 4 =$ _____

o. $8 - 0 =$ _____

p. $5 - 0 =$ _____

q. $2 - 2 =$ _____

r. $3 - 3 =$ _____

s. $0 - 0 =$ _____

Number Board

1	2	3	4	5	6	7	8	9	10
11	12	13	14	15	16	17	18	19	20
21	22	23	24	25	26	27	28	29	30
31	32	33	34	35	36	37	38	39	40
41	42	43	44	45	46	47	48	49	50
51	52	53	54	55	56	57	58	59	60
61	62	63	64	65	66	67	68	69	70
71	72	73	74	75	76	77	78	79	80
81	82	83	84	85	86	87	88	89	90
91	92	93	94	95	96	97	98	99	100
101	102	103	104	105	106	107	108	109	110
111	112	113	114	115	116	117	118	119	120
121	122	123	124	125	126	127	128	129	130

Double

Julia had 10 lollipops. She gave 5 to Lauren. How many lollipops does Julia have left?

There were 3 spoons on the table. I put some more on the table. There are now 6 spoons on the table. How many extra spoons did I put on the table?

Katie has 4 boxes. She needs 8 boxes in total. How many more boxes does she need?

There were 12 eggs in the carton and 6 of them were used to make an omelette. How many eggs are still in the carton?

There were 7 ducks in a pond. More ducks joined them. There are now 14 ducks in the pond. How many extra ducks swam into the pond?

David has 16 jelly beans. Brett has 8 jelly beans. How many more jelly beans does David have?

Double plus 1

Ella has 11 coins in her pocket. She spends 5 of them. How many coins does she have left?

Ashley's cat had 7 kittens. There are 3 male kittens. How many kittens were females?

Our chickens laid 9 eggs today, but only 4 eggs yesterday. How many more eggs did they lay today than yesterday?

Daniel had 17 marbles. He lost 8 of them. How many does he have left?

There are 8 birds sitting on the fence. More birds sit beside them. There are now 15 birds. How many extra birds sat on the fence?

Cameron has 6 toy cars. He wants to own 13 in total. How many more cars does he need?

Double plus 2

There were 12 apples in the basket. Joshua and his friends ate 5 of them. How many apples are in the basket now?

James had 4 jelly beans. His sister gave him some more. Now he has 10 jelly beans. How many did his sister give him?

Emily can have 10 friends at her party. She has invited 4 friends already. How many more friends can she invite?

Lucy blew 16 bubbles and 7 of them popped straight away. How many are left?

There were 8 balls in the box then more balls were added so that there are 14 balls in total. How many extra balls were put in the box?

I have 7 coins. Nicola has 12 coins. How many more coins does Nicola have?

Bridge to 10

Matthew had 11 balloons and 4 of them floated away. How many balloons did he have left?

Jacob found 8 shells on the beach. Then he found some more so that he had 12 in total. How many extra shells did he find?

Kayla has 11 CDs. Her friend has 7 CDs. How many more CDs does Kayla have than her friend?

There were 14 people on a bus and then 9 of them got off. How many people are left on the bus?

There were 8 books on the shelf. Natasha put some more beside them. There are now 13 books. How many books did Natasha put on the shelf?

There are 15 frogs in the pond and 6 frogs sitting beside the pond. How many more frogs are in the pond than beside the pond?

Game Board

START

FINISH

Balloons

Name: _____

Complete each number fact.

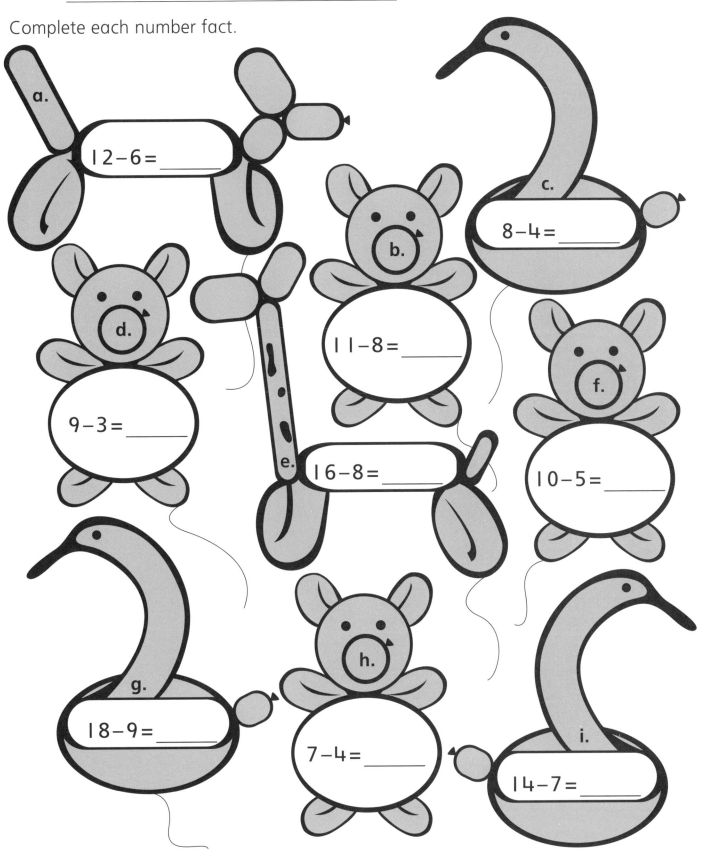

a. 12 − 6 = _____

b. 11 − 8 = _____

c. 8 − 4 = _____

d. 9 − 3 = _____

e. 16 − 8 = _____

f. 10 − 5 = _____

g. 18 − 9 = _____

h. 7 − 4 = _____

i. 14 − 7 = _____

Name: _____

Double

Write the answers as fast as you can.

$8 - 4 =$ _____

$14 - 7 =$ _____

$10 - 5 =$ _____

$18 - 9 =$ _____

$12 - 6 =$ _____

$16 - 8 =$ _____

Double plus 1

Write the answers as fast as you can.

$9 - 5 =$ _____ $17 - 8 =$ _____

$15 - 7 =$ _____ $13 - 7 =$ _____

$13 - 6 =$ _____ $9 - 4 =$ _____

$17 - 9 =$ _____ $11 - 5 =$ _____

$11 - 6 =$ _____ $15 - 8 =$ _____

Double plus 2

Write the answers as fast as you can.

$10 - 6 =$ _____ $14 - 8 =$ _____

$14 - 6 =$ _____ $12 - 5 =$ _____

$16 - 9 =$ _____ $16 - 7 =$ _____

$12 - 7 =$ _____

$10 - 4 =$ _____

Bridge to 10

Write the answers as fast as you can.

$12 - 4 =$ _____ $11 - 7 =$ _____

$14 - 9 =$ _____ $15 - 9 =$ _____

$11 - 4 =$ _____ $13 - 5 =$ _____

$15 - 6 =$ _____ $12 - 8 =$ _____

$13 - 8 =$ _____ $14 - 5 =$ _____

$13 - 4 =$ _____ $13 - 9 =$ _____

More Fact Families

Name: _____

1. Write the fact family for each domino.

a.
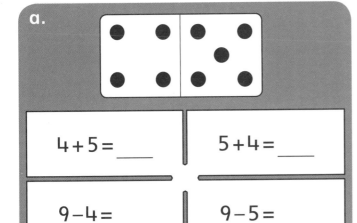

$4 + 5 =$ ___ $5 + 4 =$ ___

$9 - 4 =$ ___ $9 - 5 =$ ___

b.
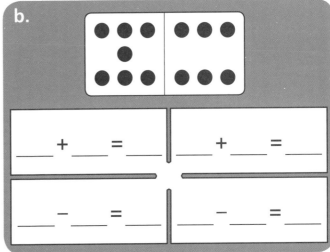

___ $+$ ___ $=$ ___   ___ $+$ ___ $=$ ___

___ $-$ ___ $=$ ___   ___ $-$ ___ $=$ ___

c.
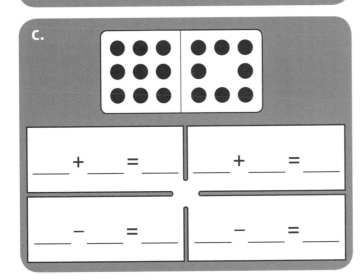

___ $+$ ___ $=$ ___   ___ $+$ ___ $=$ ___

___ $-$ ___ $=$ ___   ___ $-$ ___ $=$ ___

d.
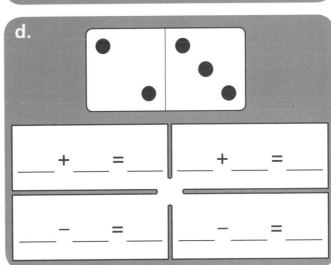

___ $+$ ___ $=$ ___   ___ $+$ ___ $=$ ___

___ $-$ ___ $=$ ___   ___ $-$ ___ $=$ ___

2. Complete these number facts and domino pictures.

a.
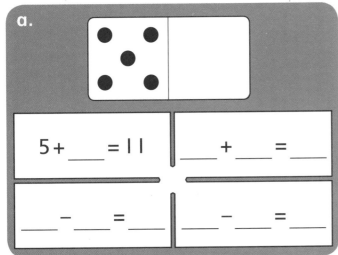

$5 +$ ___ $= 11$ ___ $+$ ___ $=$ ___

___ $-$ ___ $=$ ___   ___ $-$ ___ $=$ ___

b.
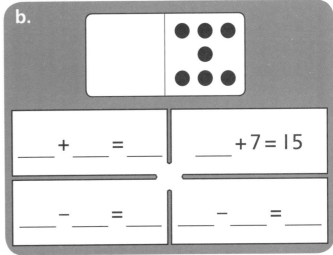

___ $+$ ___ $=$ ___   ___ $+ 7 = 15$

___ $-$ ___ $=$ ___   ___ $-$ ___ $=$ ___

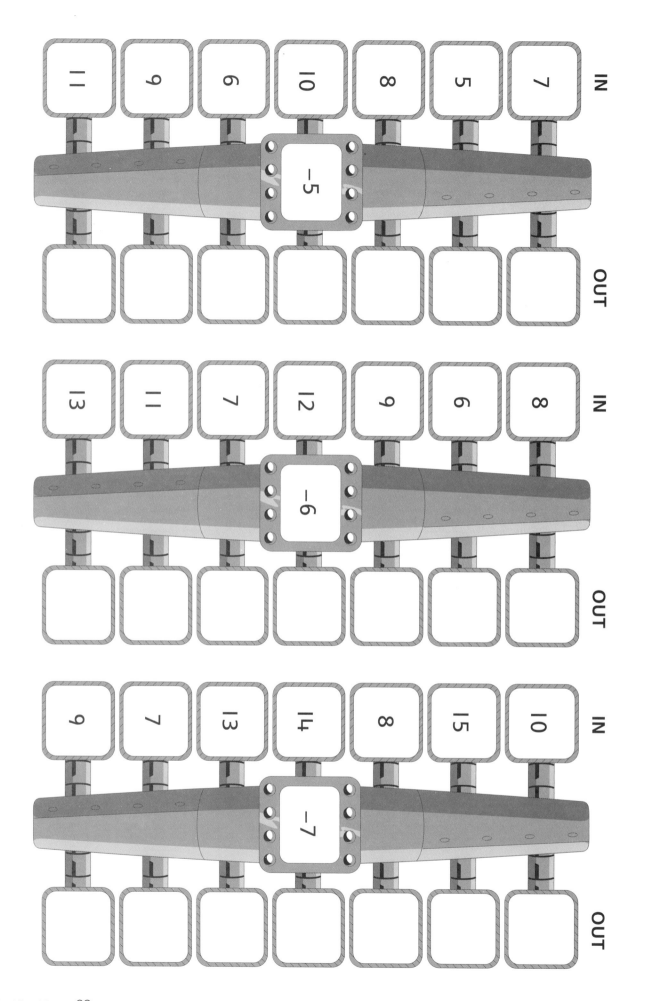

Plenty of Presents

Name: _____

Complete each number fact.

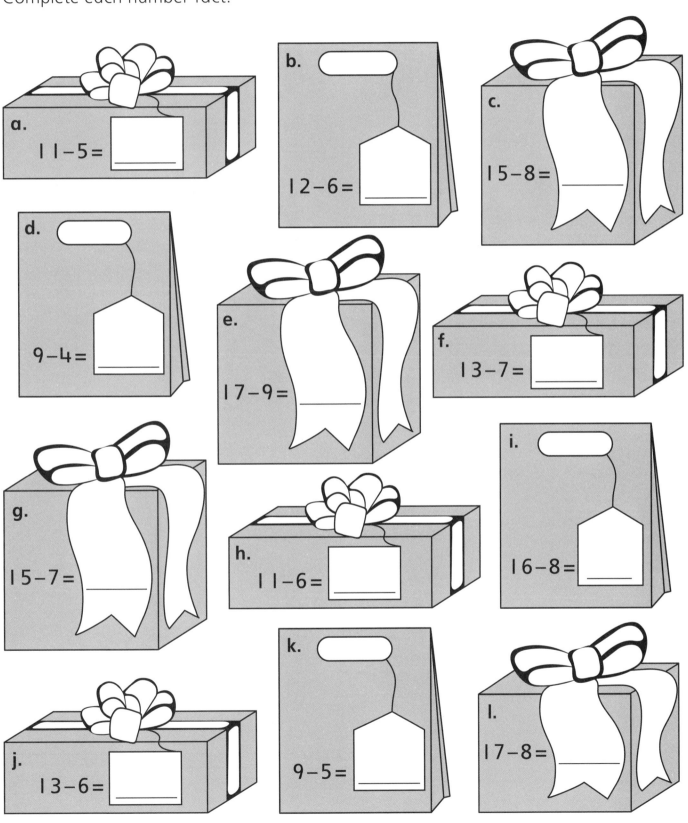

a. 11−5=

b. 12−6=

c. 15−8=

d. 9−4=

e. 17−9=

f. 13−7=

g. 15−7=

h. 11−6=

i. 16−8=

j. 13−6=

k. 9−5=

l. 17−8=

Super Spokes

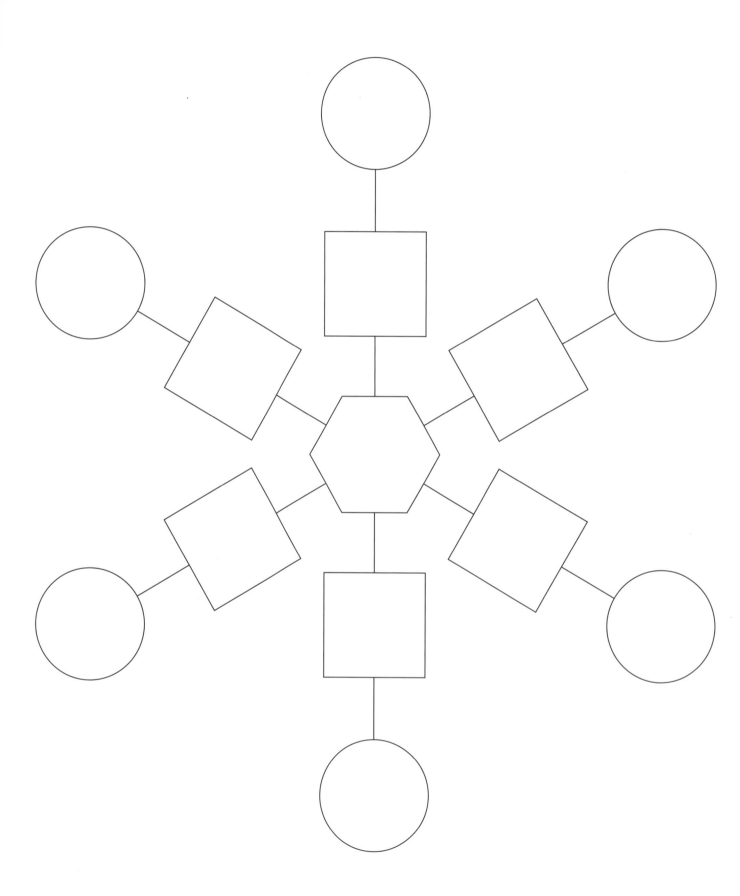

Tree House

Complete each number fact.

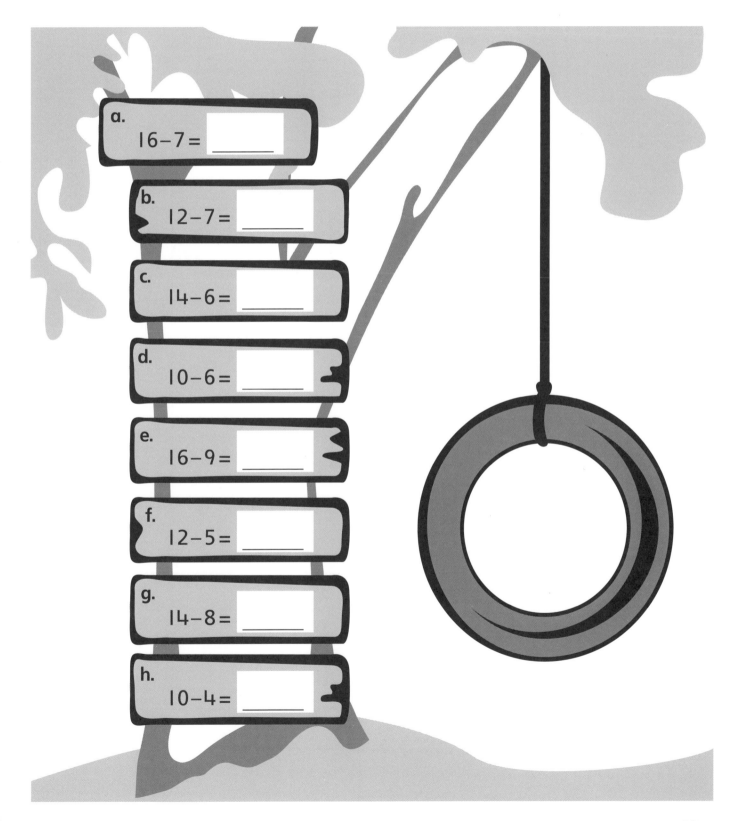

a. $16 - 7 =$ _____

b. $12 - 7 =$ _____

c. $14 - 6 =$ _____

d. $10 - 6 =$ _____

e. $16 - 9 =$ _____

f. $12 - 5 =$ _____

g. $14 - 8 =$ _____

h. $10 - 4 =$ _____

Subtraction Cover-ups

9 – 4	18 – 9	11 – 6	10 – 4	12 – 7
10 – 5	13 – 7	16 – 8	15 – 7	16 – 9
17 – 9	11 – 5	14 – 6	9 – 5	8 – 4
14 – 8	16 – 7	12 – 6	10 – 6	17 – 8
12 – 5	15 – 7	13 – 6	14 – 7	15 – 8

Lollipops

Name: _____

Complete each number fact.

12 − 8 = _____ **a.**

11 − 4 = _____ **b.**

13 − 4 = _____ **c.**

13 − 8 = _____ **d.**

15 − 9 = _____ **e.**

12 − 4 = _____ **f.**

14 − 9 = _____ **g.**

15 − 6 = _____ **h.**

13 − 9 = _____ **i.**

13 − 5 = _____ **j.**

11 − 7 = _____ **k.**

14 − 5 = _____ **l.**

Line 'em Up

1	5	8	2
3	2	6	1
7	5	3	7
4	8	6	4

Subtraction Stories

Name: _____

Read each story. Write a matching subtraction fact for each story.

a. I bought 7 apples and ate 2 of them. How many apples are left?

_____ – _____ = _____

b. Sarah had 5 marbles. Chris gave her some more. Sarah now has 8 marbles. How many marbles did Chris give Sarah?

_____ – _____ = _____

c. Matthew can have 12 friends at his party. He has invited 6 friends already. How many more friends can he invite?

_____ – _____ = _____

d. I had 6 chocolates. I ate all of them. How many do I have left?

_____ – _____ = _____

e. Joshua has 7 toy cars. He wants to own 12 in total. How many more cars does he need?

_____ – _____ = _____

f. There are 13 fish in the tank. Only 6 can be seen. How many fish are hiding?

_____ – _____ = _____

g. Emma had 9 jelly beans. Her brother gave her some more. Now she has 17 jelly beans. How many did her brother give her?

_____ – _____ = _____

h. Sophie had 12 balloons then 3 of them floated away. How many balloons did she have left?

_____ – _____ = _____

i. Emily caught 4 fish. Cameron caught 11 fish. How many more fish did Cameron catch than Emily?

_____ – _____ = _____

j. Ashley's team needs 14 points to win their game. They have scored 9 points. How many more points do they need to score?

_____ – _____ = _____

Mega Machines

Name: _____

Write the missing numbers for each machine.

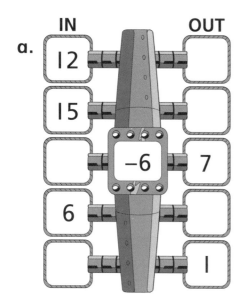

a.

IN		OUT
12		
15		
	−6	7
6		
		1

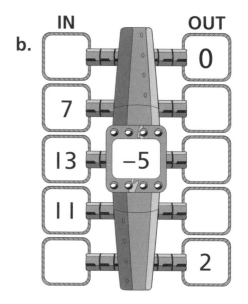

b.

IN		OUT
		0
7		
13	−5	
11		
		2

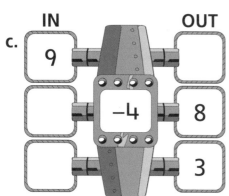

c.

IN		OUT
9		
	−4	8
		3

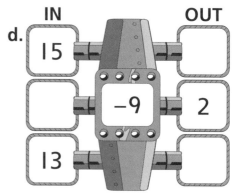

d.

IN		OUT
15		
	−9	2
13		

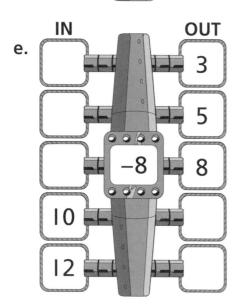

e.

IN		OUT
		3
		5
	−8	8
10		
12		

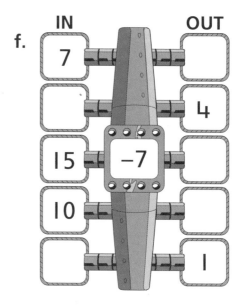

f.

IN		OUT
7		
		4
15	−7	
10		
		1